Fall into Mental Maths this Autumn with CGP!

Take a break from clearing away the leaves and put your Mental Maths knowledge to the test with this unbe-leaf-able Daily Practice book from CGP!

Inside there's a page of practice for every day of the autumn term, covering a huge range of skills from the Year 5 curriculum.

It's perfect for use in class or at home, with a fine harvest of examples and colourful pictures to keep pupils interested. Just don't leave it near a bonfire!

What CGP is all about

Our sole aim here at CGP is to produce the highest quality books — carefully written, immaculately presented and dangerously close to being funny.

Then we work our socks off to get them out to you — at the cheapest possible prices.

Contents

☑ Use the tick boxes to help keep a record of which tests have been attempted.

Week 9

Week 11

Week 10

Week 12

Published by CGP

ISBN: 978 1 78908 769 7

Editors: Ellen Burton, Emily Forsberg, Claire Plowman, Tamara Sinivassen, George Wright
With thanks to Tina Ramsden and Glenn Rogers for the proofreading.
With thanks to Lottie Edwards for the copyright research.

Clipart from Corel®

Printed by Elanders Ltd, Newcastle upon Tyne.
Based on the classic CGP style created by Richard Parsons.

How to Use this Book

- This book contains 60 daily practice tests.

- We've split them into 12 sections — that's roughly one for each week of the Year 5 autumn term.

- Each week is made up of 5 tests, so there's one for every school day of the term (Monday – Friday).

- Each test should take about 5-10 minutes to complete.

- Pupils should aim to do their working in their heads, without writing anything down.

- The tests contain a mix of Mental Maths topics from Year 4 and Year 5. New Year 5 topics are gradually introduced as you go through the book.

- The tests increase in difficulty as you progress through the term.

- Each test looks something like this:

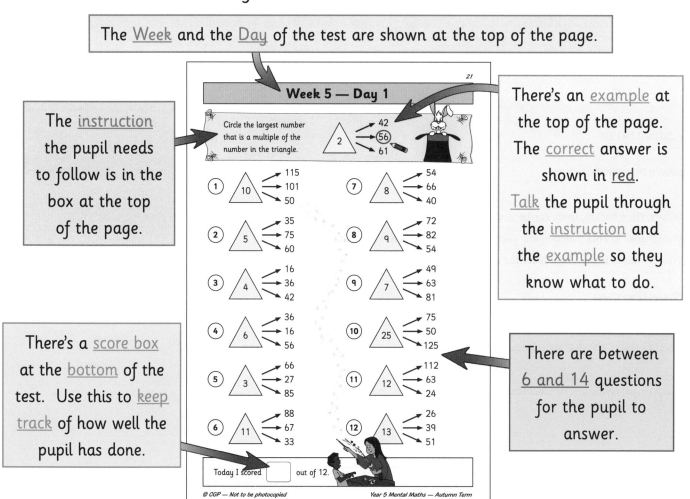

The Week and the Day of the test are shown at the top of the page.

The instruction the pupil needs to follow is in the box at the top of the page.

There's an example at the top of the page. The correct answer is shown in red. Talk the pupil through the instruction and the example so they know what to do.

There's a score box at the bottom of the test. Use this to keep track of how well the pupil has done.

There are between 6 and 14 questions for the pupil to answer.

Week 1 — Day 1

Write down the coordinates of the point on the grid.

(4, 3)

1

5

2

6

3

7

4

8

Today I scored ☐ out of 8.

Year 5 Mental Maths — Autumn Term

Week 1 — Day 2

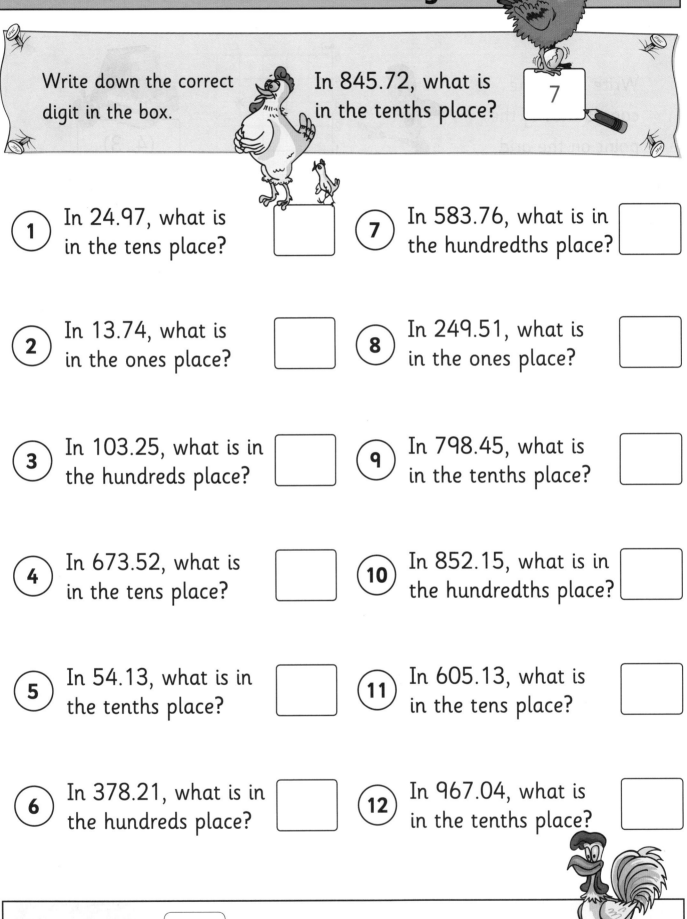

Write down the correct digit in the box.

In 845.72, what is in the tenths place? **7**

(1) In 24.97, what is in the tens place?

(2) In 13.74, what is in the ones place?

(3) In 103.25, what is in the hundreds place?

(4) In 673.52, what is in the tens place?

(5) In 54.13, what is in the tenths place?

(6) In 378.21, what is in the hundreds place?

(7) In 583.76, what is in the hundredths place?

(8) In 249.51, what is in the ones place?

(9) In 798.45, what is in the tenths place?

(10) In 852.15, what is in the hundredths place?

(11) In 605.13, what is in the tens place?

(12) In 967.04, what is in the tenths place?

Today I scored ☐ out of 12.

Week 1 — Day 3

Circle the larger volume of water.

248 ml   (2.4 l)

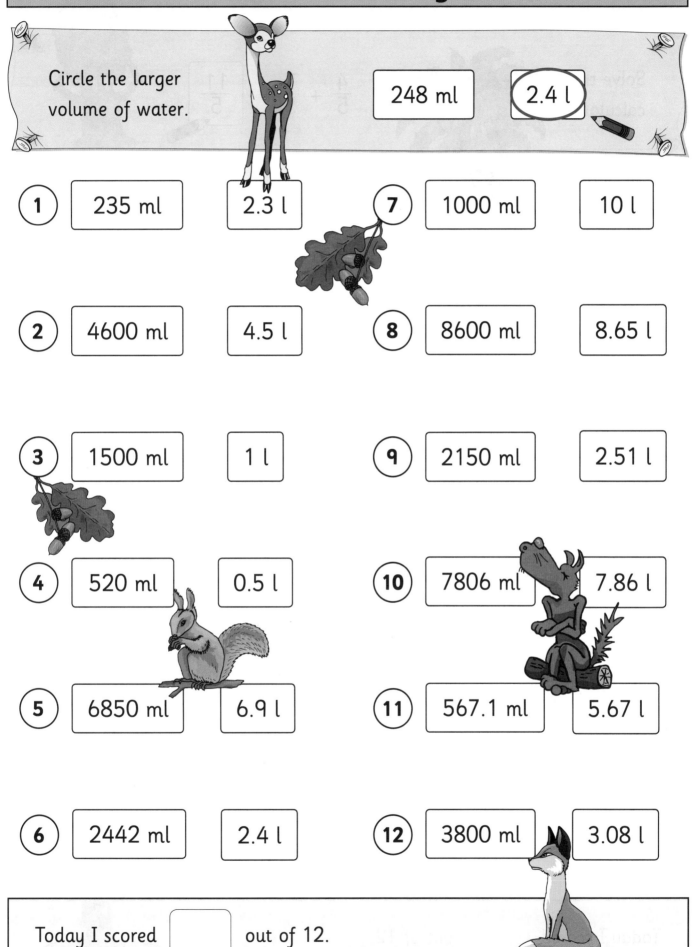

1 | 235 ml | 2.3 l

7 | 1000 ml | 10 l

2 | 4600 ml | 4.5 l

8 | 8600 ml | 8.65 l

3 | 1500 ml | 1 l

9 | 2150 ml | 2.51 l

4 | 520 ml | 0.5 l

10 | 7806 ml | 7.86 l

5 | 6850 ml | 6.9 l

11 | 567.1 ml | 5.67 l

6 | 2442 ml | 2.4 l

12 | 3800 ml | 3.08 l

Today I scored [   ] out of 12.

Year 5 Mental Maths — Autumn Term

Week 1 — Day 4

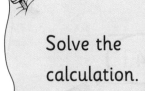

Solve the calculation.

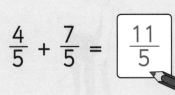

$\frac{4}{5} + \frac{7}{5} = \boxed{\frac{11}{5}}$

(1) $\frac{4}{9} + \frac{6}{9} = \boxed{}$

(7) $\frac{4}{40} + \frac{14}{40} + \frac{2}{40} = \boxed{}$

(2) $\frac{7}{11} - \frac{3}{11} = \boxed{}$

(8) $\frac{27}{45} - \frac{17}{45} - \frac{3}{45} = \boxed{}$

(3) $\frac{15}{10} + \frac{6}{10} = \boxed{}$

(9) $\frac{15}{60} + \frac{7}{60} + \frac{3}{60} = \boxed{}$

(4) $\frac{13}{6} - \frac{4}{6} = \boxed{}$

(10) $\frac{89}{75} - \frac{20}{75} - \frac{29}{75} = \boxed{}$

(5) $\frac{14}{5} + \frac{3}{5} + \frac{2}{5} = \boxed{}$

(11) $\frac{12}{28} + \frac{18}{28} + \frac{9}{28} = \boxed{}$

(6) $\frac{13}{15} - \frac{3}{15} - \frac{1}{15} = \boxed{}$

(12) $\frac{92}{89} - \frac{12}{89} - \frac{20}{89} = \boxed{}$

Today I scored $\boxed{}$ out of 12.

Week 1 — Day 5

Circle the number that matches the Roman numeral.

III → ③

III → 8

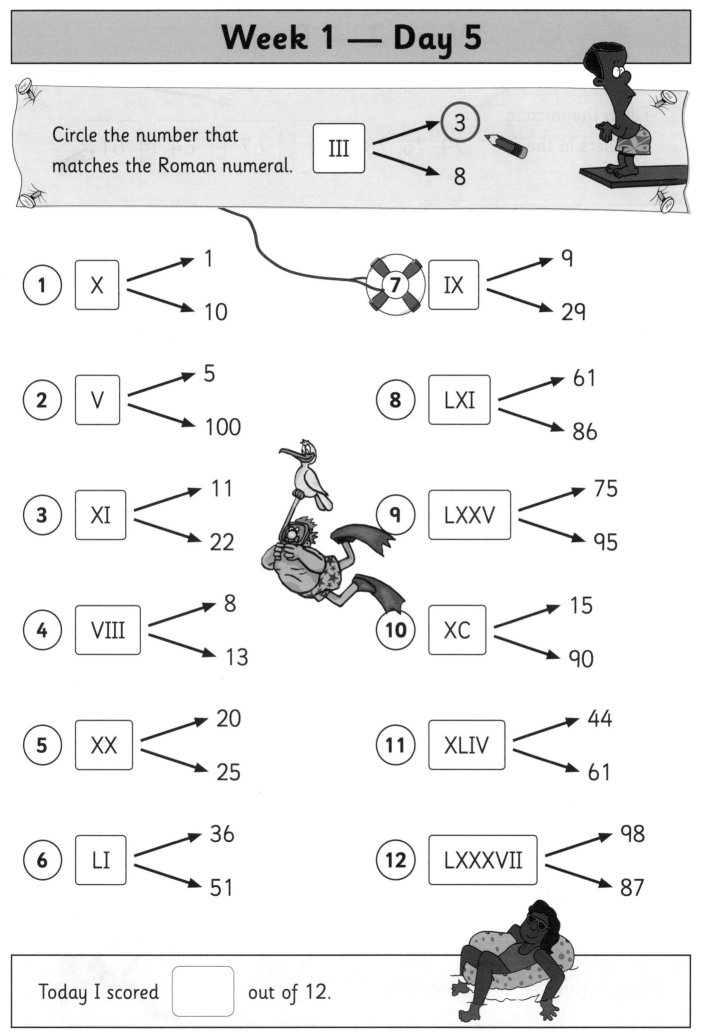

1 X → 1

X → 10

2 V → 5

V → 100

3 XI → 11

XI → 22

4 VIII → 8

VIII → 13

5 XX → 20

XX → 25

6 LI → 36

LI → 51

7 IX → 9

IX → 29

8 LXI → 61

LXI → 86

9 LXXV → 75

LXXV → 95

10 XC → 15

XC → 90

11 XLIV → 44

XLIV → 61

12 LXXXVII → 98

LXXXVII → 87

Today I scored [ ] out of 12.

Year 5 Mental Maths — Autumn Term

Week 2 — Day 1

Fill in the missing numbers in the sequence.

79, 76, 73, 70 , 67 , 64 , 61

1 9, 14, 19, ☐ , ☐ , ☐ , ☐

2 135, 115, 95, ☐ , ☐ , ☐ , ☐

3 112, 2112, 4112, ☐ , ☐ , ☐ , ☐

4 228, 234, 240, ☐ , ☐ , ☐ , ☐

5 525, 550, 575, ☐ , ☐ , ☐ , ☐

6 3442, 3462, 3482, ☐ , ☐ , ☐ , ☐

7 860, 854, 848, ☐ , ☐ , ☐ , ☐

8 490, 475, 460, ☐ , ☐ , ☐ , ☐

Today I scored ☐ out of 8.

Week 2 — Day 2

Add together the prices on the café receipt.

Apple juice	£0.90
Crisps	£0.80

£1.70

1 Coffee £1.20 / Muffin £2.10

£

2 Hot chocolate £3.20 / Cheese panini £5.30

£

3 Lemonade £1.10 / Bakewell tart £4.40

£

4 Green tea £1.60 / Fruit scone £5.40

£

5 Blueberry smoothie £3.70 / Brownie £4.50

£

6 Ice cream £2.60 / Flapjack £4.50

£

7 Tomato soup £4.10 / Potato salad £2.90

£

8 Battered fish £3.80 / Chips £2.40

£

9 Mushroom burger £6.90 / Green salad £1.40

£

10 Spicy bean wrap £7.20 / Cola £2.90

£

Today I scored [ ] out of 10.

Year 5 Mental Maths — Autumn Term

Week 2 — Day 3

Circle the equivalent fraction.

$$\frac{6}{8} \nearrow \frac{2}{3}$$
$$\searrow \boxed{\frac{3}{4}}$$

1 $\frac{4}{8}$ $\nearrow \frac{1}{4}$ $\searrow \frac{1}{2}$

2 $\frac{3}{9}$ $\nearrow \frac{1}{6}$ $\searrow \frac{1}{3}$

3 $\frac{2}{10}$ $\nearrow \frac{1}{5}$ $\searrow \frac{2}{7}$

4 $\frac{4}{16}$ $\nearrow \frac{1}{8}$ $\searrow \frac{1}{4}$

5 $\frac{6}{18}$ $\nearrow \frac{1}{3}$ $\searrow \frac{1}{4}$

6 $\frac{3}{12}$ $\nearrow \frac{1}{4}$ $\searrow \frac{1}{3}$

7 $\frac{5}{25}$ $\nearrow \frac{1}{5}$ $\searrow \frac{1}{15}$

8 $\frac{11}{66}$ $\nearrow \frac{1}{11}$ $\searrow \frac{1}{6}$

9 $\frac{4}{6}$ $\nearrow \frac{3}{4}$ $\searrow \frac{2}{3}$

10 $\frac{6}{24}$ $\nearrow \frac{2}{8}$ $\searrow \frac{2}{4}$

Today I scored [ ] out of 10.

Week 2 — Day 4

Work out the answer to the subtraction.

$1000 - 150 = \boxed{850}$

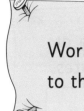

1 $164 - 20 = \boxed{}$

2 $265 - 32 = \boxed{}$

3 $342 - 21 = \boxed{}$

4 $650 - 45 = \boxed{}$

5 $851 - 35 = \boxed{}$

6 $649 - 50 = \boxed{}$

7 $650 - 140 = \boxed{}$

8 $265 - 145 = \boxed{}$

9 $900 - 260 = \boxed{}$

10 $735 - 140 = \boxed{}$

11 $859 - 241 = \boxed{}$

12 $412 - 77 = \boxed{}$

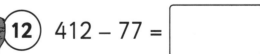

Today I scored $\boxed{}$ out of 12.

Year 5 Mental Maths — Autumn Term

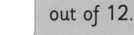

Week 2 — Day 5

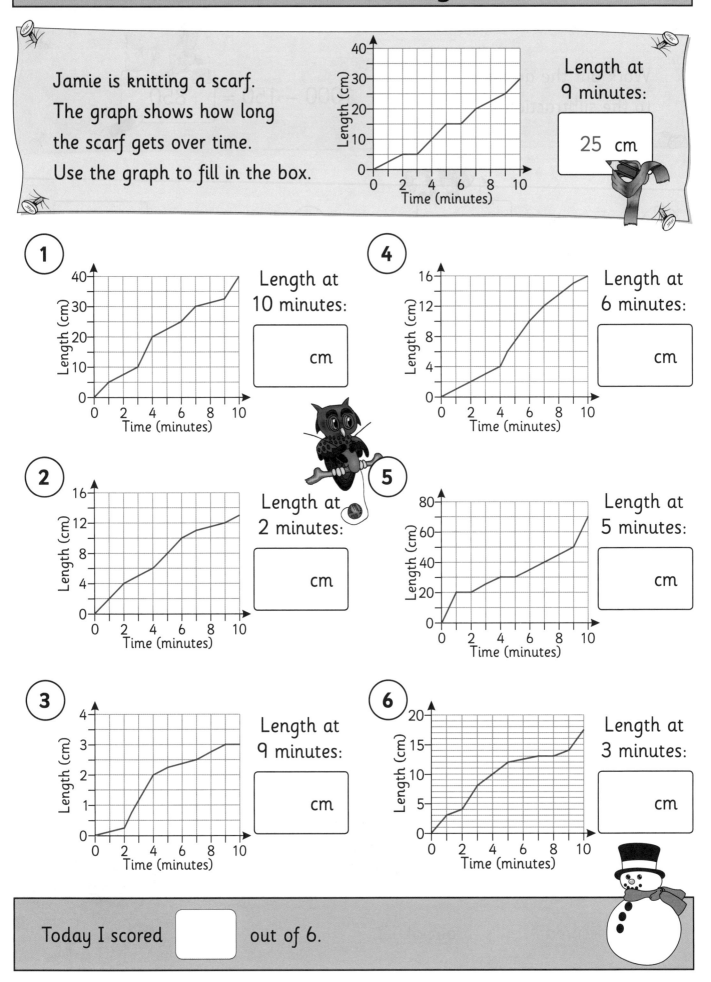

Jamie is knitting a scarf.
The graph shows how long
the scarf gets over time.
Use the graph to fill in the box.

Length at
9 minutes:

25 cm

1 Length at 10 minutes:

cm

2 Length at 2 minutes:

cm

3 Length at 9 minutes:

cm

4 Length at 6 minutes:

cm

5 Length at 5 minutes:

cm

6 Length at 3 minutes:

cm

Today I scored ☐ out of 6.

Week 3 — Day 1

The start and finish times for a race are given. How long did it take to complete the race?

Start: 10:20
Finish: 11:56

1 hour 36 minutes

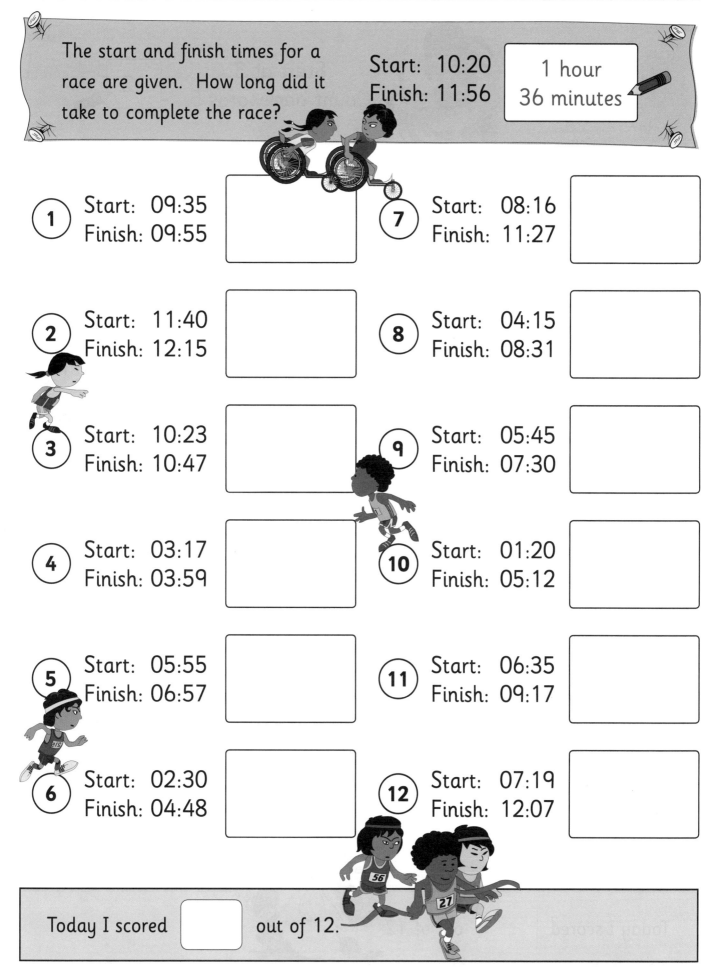

1 Start: 09:35
Finish: 09:55

7 Start: 08:16
Finish: 11:27

2 Start: 11:40
Finish: 12:15

8 Start: 04:15
Finish: 08:31

3 Start: 10:23
Finish: 10:47

9 Start: 05:45
Finish: 07:30

4 Start: 03:17
Finish: 03:59

10 Start: 01:20
Finish: 05:12

5 Start: 05:55
Finish: 06:57

11 Start: 06:35
Finish: 09:17

6 Start: 02:30
Finish: 04:48

12 Start: 07:19
Finish: 12:07

Today I scored ☐ out of 12.

Year 5 Mental Maths — Autumn Term

Week 3 — Day 2

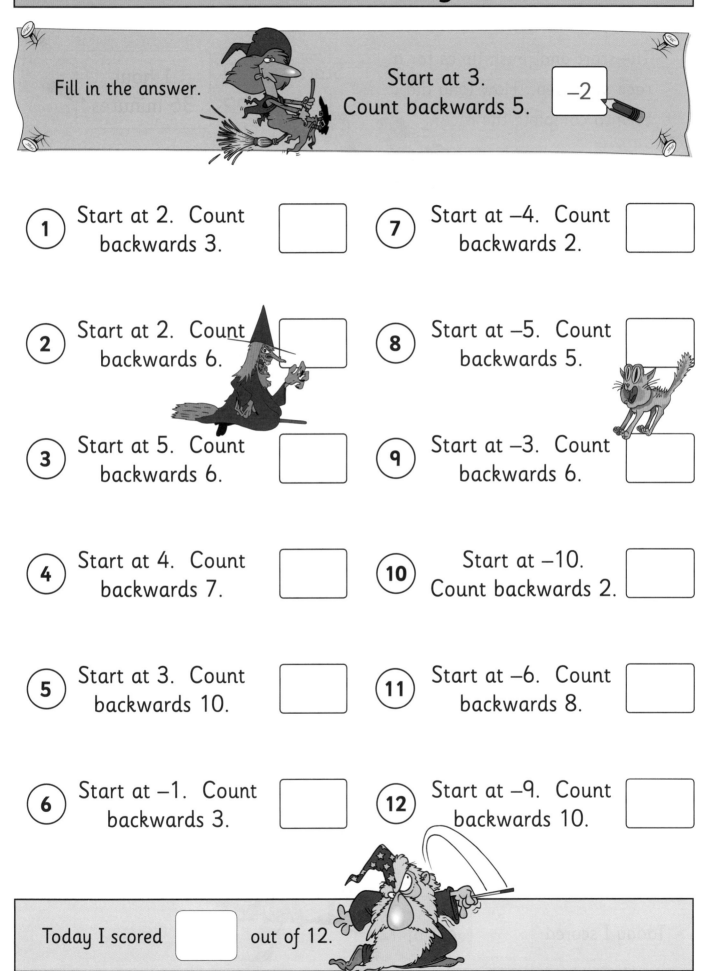

Fill in the answer.

Start at 3.
Count backwards 5.

-2

1 Start at 2. Count backwards 3.

7 Start at −4. Count backwards 2.

2 Start at 2. Count backwards 6.

8 Start at −5. Count backwards 5.

3 Start at 5. Count backwards 6.

9 Start at −3. Count backwards 6.

4 Start at 4. Count backwards 7.

10 Start at −10. Count backwards 2.

5 Start at 3. Count backwards 10.

11 Start at −6. Count backwards 8.

6 Start at −1. Count backwards 3.

12 Start at −9. Count backwards 10.

Today I scored ___ out of 12.

Week 3 — Day 3

Calculate the perimeter of the shape. (The shapes are not drawn to scale.)

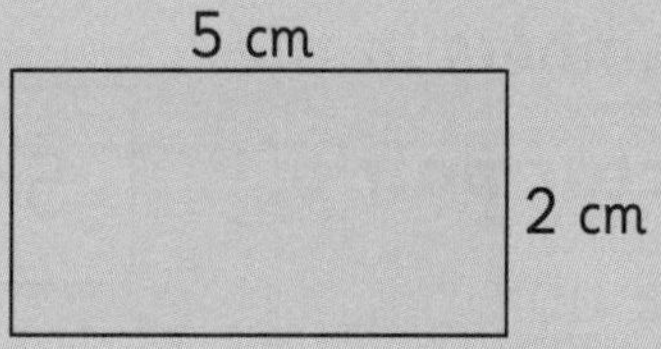

5 cm

2 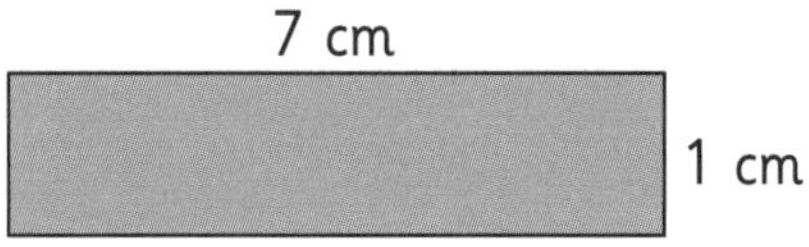 cm

14 cm

1 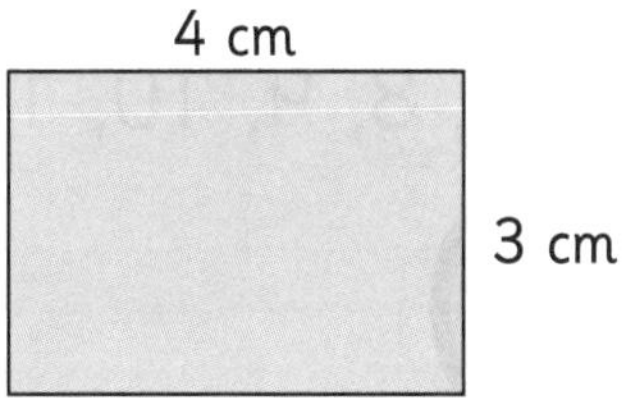 4 cm / 3 cm

cm

5 9 cm / 8 cm

cm

2 7 cm / 1 cm

cm

6 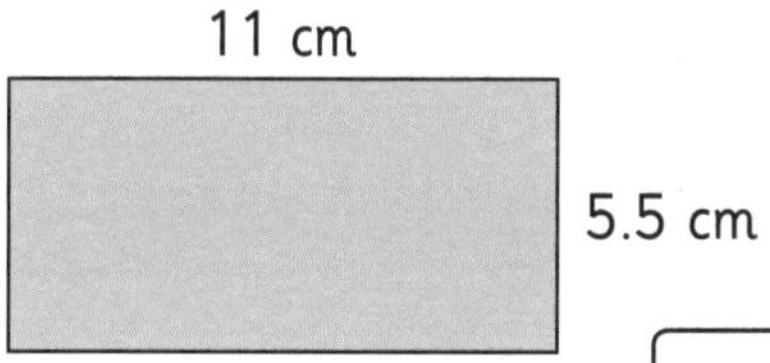 11 cm / 5.5 cm

cm

3 7 cm / 3 cm

cm

7 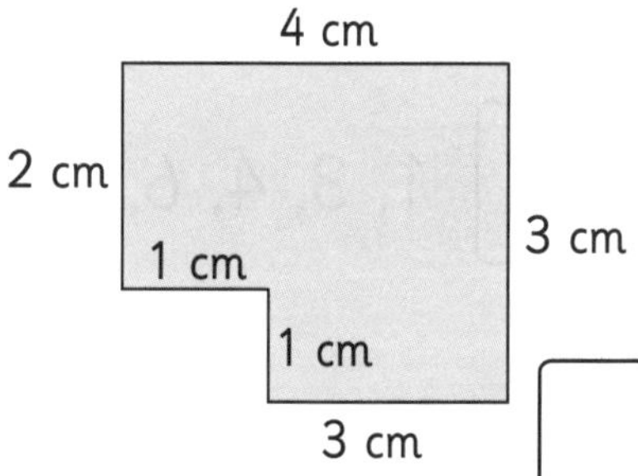 4 cm / 2 cm / 1 cm / 1 cm / 3 cm / 3 cm

cm

4 3.5 cm / 8 cm

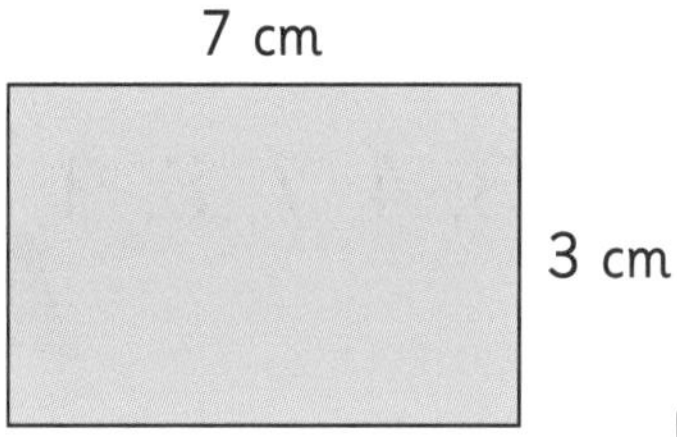

cm

8 5 cm / 4 cm / 2 cm / 2 cm  / 4 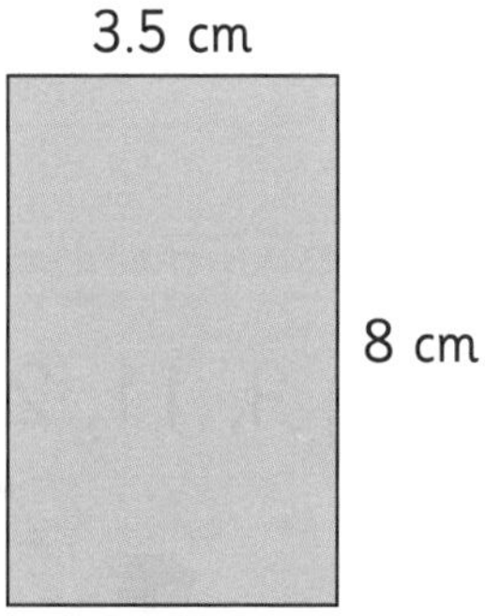 cm / 5 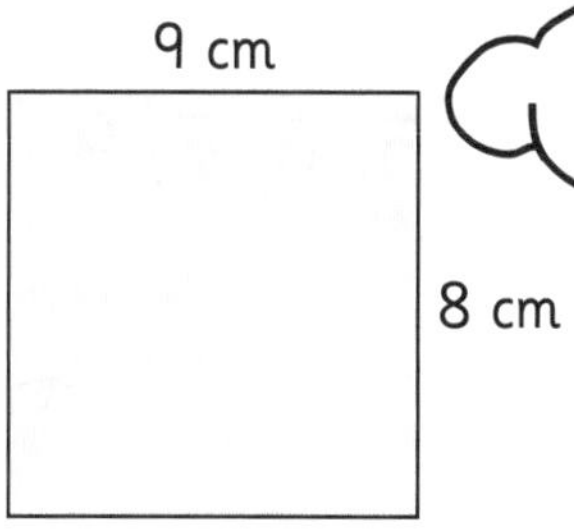 cm

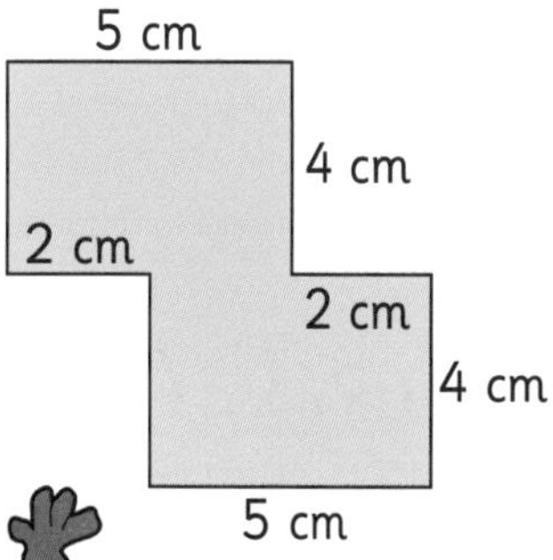

cm

Today I scored [ ] out of 8.

Year 5 Mental Maths — Autumn Term

Week 3 — Day 4

Circle the **two** numbers in the list that are a **factor pair** of the number in the box.

54 | 2, 4, ⑥ 8, ⑨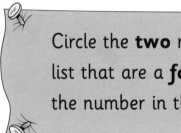

(1) 18 | 2, 5, 6, 7, 9

(7) 40 | 4, 8, 9, 10, 15

(2) 20 | 1, 3, 4, 5, 15

(8) 36 | 4, 8, 9, 12, 36

(3) 24 | 2, 3, 6, 8, 10

(9) 44 | 2, 6, 8, 11, 22

(4) 30 | 1, 3, 4, 6, 30

(10) 56 | 3, 4, 7, 8, 9

(5) 32 | 3, 4, 8, 9, 12

(11) 72 | 2, 3, 4, 8, 9

(6) 35 | 1, 5, 6, 7, 15

(12) 88 | 4, 8, 9, 11, 20

Today I scored [ ] out of 12.

Week 3 — Day 5

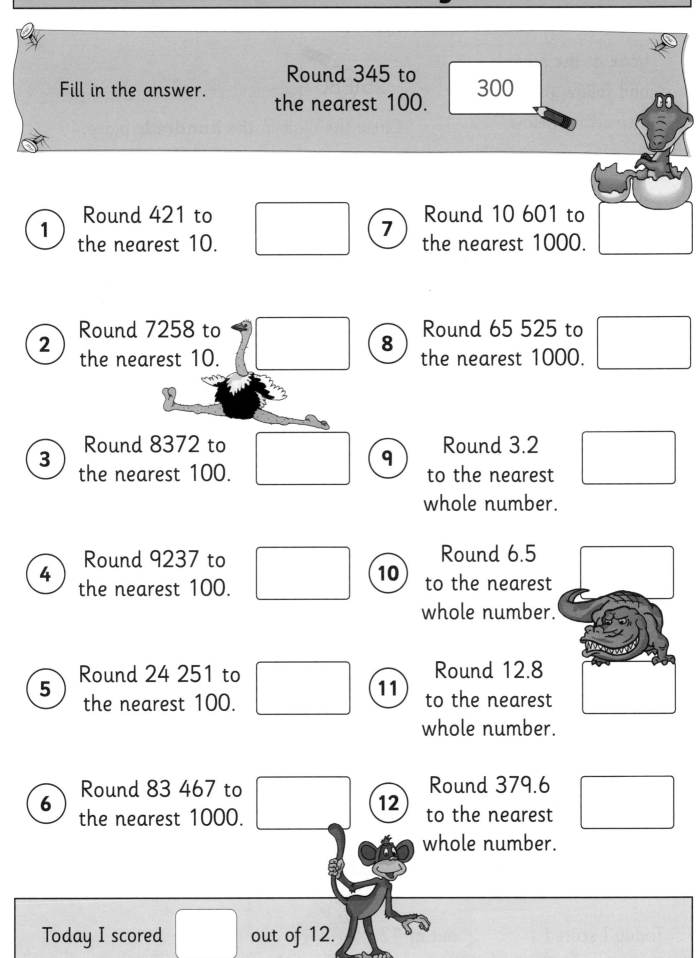

Fill in the answer.

Round 345 to the nearest 100.

300

1 Round 421 to the nearest 10.

2 Round 7258 to the nearest 10.

3 Round 8372 to the nearest 100.

4 Round 9237 to the nearest 100.

5 Round 24 251 to the nearest 100.

6 Round 83 467 to the nearest 1000.

7 Round 10 601 to the nearest 1000.

8 Round 65 525 to the nearest 1000.

9 Round 3.2 to the nearest whole number.

10 Round 6.5 to the nearest whole number.

11 Round 12.8 to the nearest whole number.

12 Round 379.6 to the nearest whole number.

Today I scored [ ] out of 12.

Year 5 Mental Maths — Autumn Term

Week 4 — Day 1

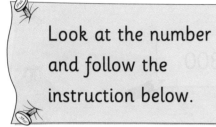

Look at the number and follow the instruction below.

25⑧60

Circle the digit in the **hundreds** place.

1 3268

Circle the digit in the **hundreds** place.

2 5356

Circle the digit in the **thousands** place.

3 38 223

Circle the digit in the **tens** place.

4 47 023

Circle the digit in the **thousands** place.

5 486 228

Circle the digit in the **hundred thousands** place.

6 890 012

Circle the digit in the **ten thousands** place.

7 360 237

Circle the digit in the **thousands** place.

8 472 489

Circle the digit in the **tens** place.

9 1 720 300

Circle the digit in the **thousands** place.

10 1 112 783

Circle the digit in the **millions** place.

11 2 046 237

Circle the digit in the **hundred thousands** place.

12 7 234 545

Circle the digit in the **ten thousands** place.

Today I scored ☐ out of 12.

Week 4 — Day 2

Write the number using digits.

One thousand, seven hundred and thirty nine

1739

1 Three thousand, four hundred and twenty eight

5 Thirty three thousand and ninety

2 Forty two thousand, three hundred and eleven

6 Seven hundred and fourteen thousand, two hundred and four

3 Three hundred and forty thousand, two hundred and seventy five

7 Eight hundred thousand and three

4 One hundred and three thousand and sixty nine

8 Four hundred and twelve thousand and sixty

Today I scored [ ] out of 8.

Year 5 Mental Maths — Autumn Term

Week 4 — Day 3

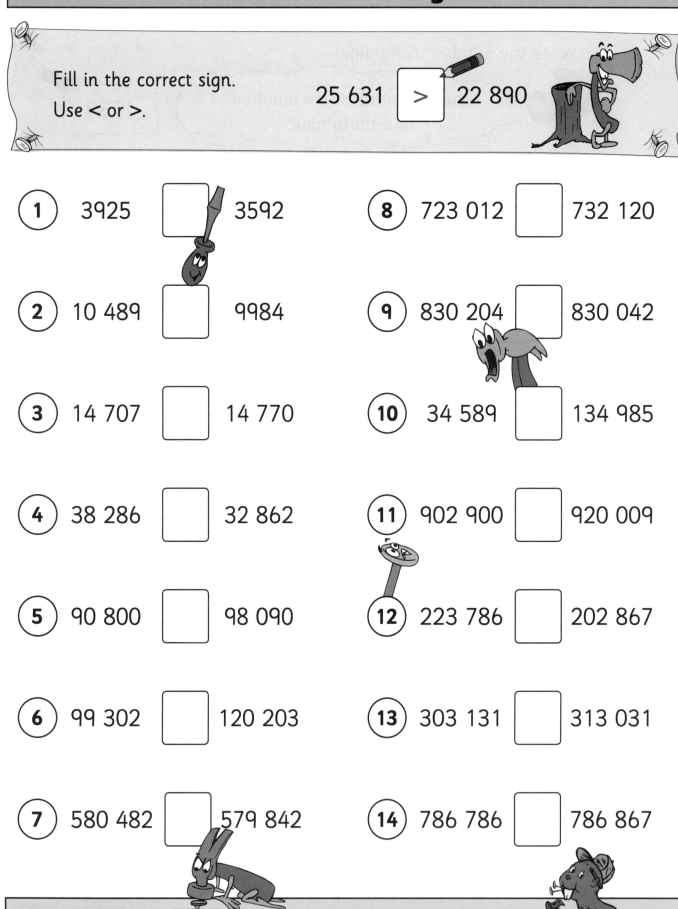

Fill in the correct sign.
Use < or >.

25 631 $\boxed{>}$ 22 890

(1) 3925 $\boxed{\phantom{<}}$ 3592

(2) 10 489 $\boxed{\phantom{<}}$ 9984

(3) 14 707 $\boxed{\phantom{<}}$ 14 770

(4) 38 286 $\boxed{\phantom{<}}$ 32 862

(5) 90 800 $\boxed{\phantom{<}}$ 98 090

(6) 99 302 $\boxed{\phantom{<}}$ 120 203

(7) 580 482 $\boxed{\phantom{<}}$ 579 842

(8) 723 012 $\boxed{\phantom{<}}$ 732 120

(9) 830 204 $\boxed{\phantom{<}}$ 830 042

(10) 34 589 $\boxed{\phantom{<}}$ 134 985

(11) 902 900 $\boxed{\phantom{<}}$ 920 009

(12) 223 786 $\boxed{\phantom{<}}$ 202 867

(13) 303 131 $\boxed{\phantom{<}}$ 313 031

(14) 786 786 $\boxed{\phantom{<}}$ 786 867

Today I scored $\boxed{}$ out of 14.

Year 5 Mental Maths — Autumn Term

© *CGP — Not to be photocopied*

Week 4 — Day 4

Fill in the missing number in the sequence.

2387 , 2487 , 2587 , 2687

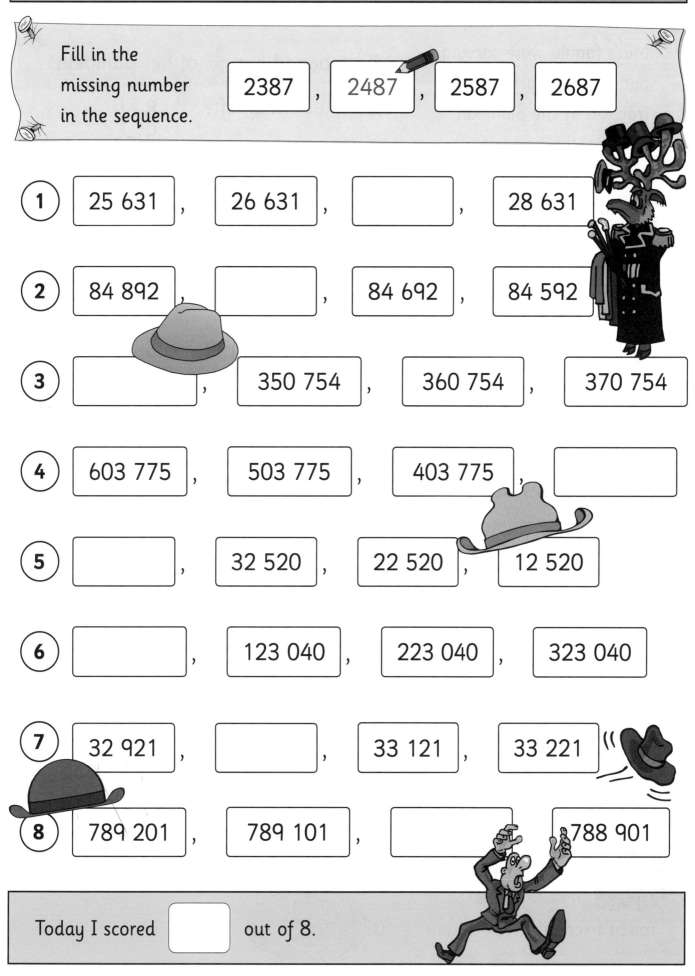

1) 25 631 , 26 631 , _____ , 28 631

2) 84 892 , _____ , 84 692 , 84 592

3) _____ , 350 754 , 360 754 , 370 754

4) 603 775 , 503 775 , 403 775 , _____

5) _____ , 32 520 , 22 520 , 12 520

6) _____ , 123 040 , 223 040 , 323 040

7) 32 921 , _____ , 33 121 , 33 221

8) 789 201 , 789 101 , _____ , 788 901

Today I scored _____ out of 8.

Year 5 Mental Maths — Autumn Term

Week 4 — Day 5

Mia's family were carving pumpkins. Work out the fraction of the pumpkin each person had left.

Mia scooped out $\frac{1}{9}$ of her pumpkin. How much was left? $\frac{8}{9}$

① Mum scooped out $\frac{1}{3}$ of her pumpkin. How much was left?

② Dad scooped out $\frac{2}{5}$ of his pumpkin. How much was left?

③ Big sister scooped out $\frac{3}{7}$ of her pumpkin. How much was left?

④ Little brother scooped out $\frac{5}{8}$ of his pumpkin. How much was left?

⑤ Nana scooped out $\frac{2}{11}$ of her pumpkin. How much was left?

⑥ Gramps scooped out $\frac{7}{12}$ of his pumpkin. How much was left?

⑦ Aunt Flo scooped out $\frac{9}{16}$ of her pumpkin. How much was left?

⑧ Uncle Bob scooped out $\frac{17}{20}$ of his pumpkin. How much was left?

⑨ Great Aunt Bee scooped out $\frac{6}{21}$ of her pumpkin. How much was left?

⑩ The cat scooped out $\frac{17}{29}$ of his pumpkin. How much was left?

Today I scored [ ] out of 10.

Week 5 — Day 1

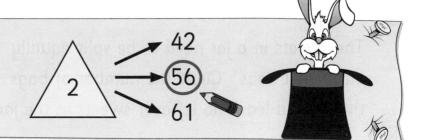

Circle the largest number that is a multiple of the number in the triangle.

Example: Triangle with 2 → 42, 56 (circled), 61

1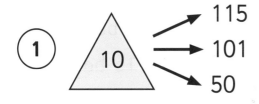
10 → 115, 101, 50

2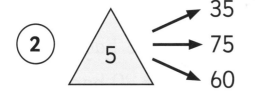
5 → 35, 75, 60

3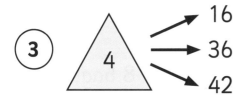
4 → 16, 36, 42

4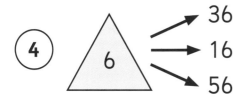
6 → 36, 16, 56

5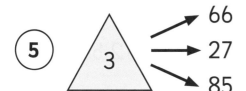
3 → 66, 27, 85

6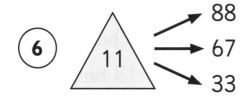
11 → 88, 67, 33

7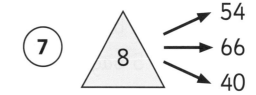
8 → 54, 66, 40

8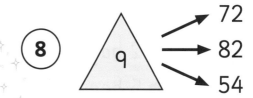
9 → 72, 82, 54

9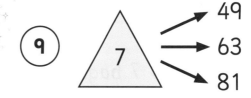
7 → 49, 63, 81

10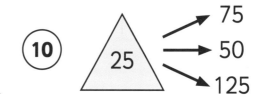
25 → 75, 50, 125

11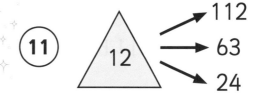
12 → 112, 63, 24

12
13 → 26, 39, 51

Today I scored [ ] out of 12.

Year 5 Mental Maths — Autumn Term

Week 5 — Day 2

The sweets in a jar need to be split equally into small bags. Circle the number of bags that would leave no leftover sweets in the jar.

56 sweets → **7 bags** / 9 bags / 10 bags

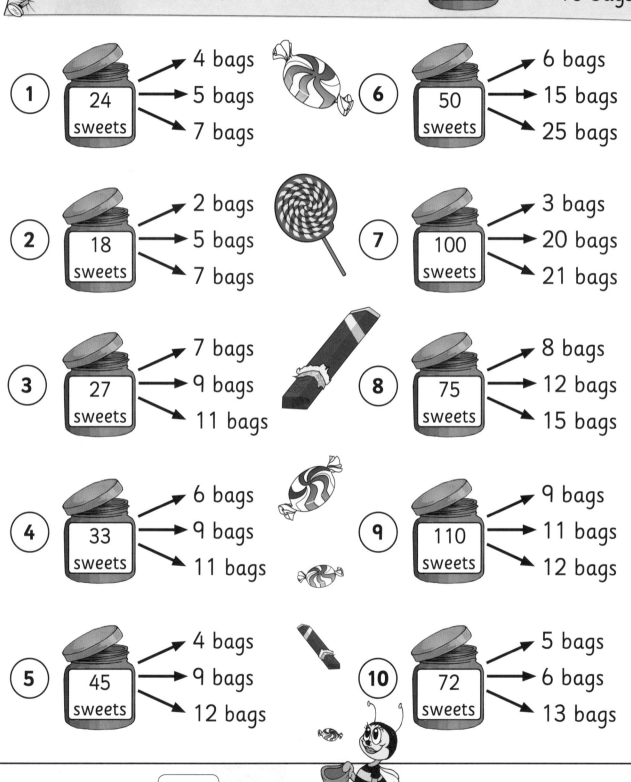

1 24 sweets → 4 bags / 5 bags / 7 bags

6 50 sweets → 6 bags / 15 bags / 25 bags

2 18 sweets → 2 bags / 5 bags / 7 bags

7 100 sweets → 3 bags / 20 bags / 21 bags

3 27 sweets → 7 bags / 9 bags / 11 bags

8 75 sweets → 8 bags / 12 bags / 15 bags

4 33 sweets → 6 bags / 9 bags / 11 bags

9 110 sweets → 9 bags / 11 bags / 12 bags

5 45 sweets → 4 bags / 9 bags / 12 bags

10 72 sweets → 5 bags / 6 bags / 13 bags

Today I scored ☐ out of 10.

Week 5 — Day 3

Some factor pairs for each number have been given.
Write down the missing factor pair.

Factor pairs of 12:
1 × 12, 2 × 6

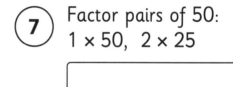

3 × 4

1 Factor pairs of 15:
1 × 15

6 Factor pairs of 45:
1 × 45, 3 × 15

2 Factor pairs of 24:
1 × 24, 2 × 12, 4 × 6

7 Factor pairs of 50:
1 × 50, 2 × 25

3 Factor pairs of 28:
1 × 28, 2 × 14

8 Factor pairs of 66:
1 × 66, 3 × 22, 6 × 11

4 Factor pairs of 27:
1 × 27

9 Factor pairs of 100:
1 × 100, 2 × 50, 5 × 20,
10 × 10

5 Factor pairs of 56:
1 × 56, 2 × 28, 4 × 14

10 Factor pairs of 72:
1 × 72, 2 × 36, 4 × 18,
6 × 12, 8 × 9

Today I scored [ ] out of 10.

Year 5 Mental Maths — Autumn Term

Week 5 — Day 4

Add together the two prices.

£10 000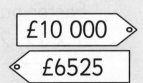
£6525

£16 525

1 £15 000
£54

£

7 £54 000
£11 020

£

2 £20 000
£13 000

£

8 £41 205
£41 300

£

3 £95 000
£325

£

9 £87 100
£1005

£

4 £68 000
£21 000

£

10 £53 200
£3003

£

5 £13 400
£6000

£

11 £11 050
£11 050

£

6 £32 100
£7340

£

12 £52 102
£10 101

£

Today I scored [ ] out of 12.

Week 5 — Day 5

Write down the number in the rain that is a common factor of the two numbers in the cloud.

 1

 6

 2

 7

3

 8

4 36 28

 9

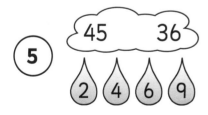 5

 10

Today I scored ☐ out of 10.

Year 5 Mental Maths — Autumn Term

Week 6 — Day 1

Which point on the grid has these coordinates? Circle the correct letter.

(4, 4)

A   B   Ⓒ

1

(3, 3)

A   B   C

2

(3, 0)

A   B   C

3

(5, 1)

A   B   C

4

(5, 4)

A   B   C

5

(0, 2)

A   B   C

6

(4, 6)

A   B   C

Today I scored ⬜ out of 6.

Week 6 — Day 2

Circle the best estimate for the measurement.

The weight of a cow.

| 0.72 kg | 7.2 kg | (720 kg) |

(1) The height of a bookcase.

| 2 m | 20 m | 200 m |

(7) The amount of paint in a tin.

| 5 l | 50 l | 500 l |

(2) The height of a 9-year-old child.

| 13 cm | 130 cm | 1.3 cm |

(8) The amount of tea in a full mug.

| 30 ml | 3 ml | 300 ml |

(3) The weight of an apple.

| 1.8 g | 18 g | 180 g |

(9) The weight of a kitten.

| 1.5 g | 15 g | 150 g |

(4) The height of a sunflower.

| 2.5 m | 25 m | 250 m |

(10) The weight of a full cereal box.

| 0.5 g | 500 g | 50 g |

(5) The length of a tennis court.

| 24 m | 240 m | 2.4 m |

(11) The width of a fire engine.

| 2.3 m | 23 m | 0.23 m |

(6) The weight of a watermelon.

| 10 kg | 100 kg | 0.1 kg |

(12) The amount of water in a full bucket.

| 100 l | 10 l | 0.1 l |

Today I scored [ ] out of 12.

Week 6 — Day 3

Work out the answer to the subtraction.

15 000 − 4500 = ?

10 500

1 9000 − 2000 = ?

2 8000 − 6000 = ?

3 10 000 − 7000 = ?

4 40 000 − 9000 = ?

5 68 000 − 8000 = ?

6 58 000 − 10 000 = ?

7 37 000 − 30 000 = ?

8 47 000 − 12 000 = ?

9 86 000 − 12 000 = ?

10 79 000 − 23 000 = ?

11 92 000 − 41 000 = ?

12 98 000 − 63 000 = ?

Today I scored ☐ out of 12.

Week 6 — Day 4

Look at George and Elsie's answers to the calculation. Using rounding to check, circle the most sensible answer.

20.2 − 15.4 = ?

George: "The answer is 4.8."

Elsie: "The answer is 6.3."

1 523 − 198 = ?

George: "The answer is 235."

Elsie: "The answer is 325."

5 26.6 − 11.8 = ?

George: "The answer is 14.8."

Elsie: "The answer is 13.7."

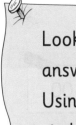

2 689 − 416 = ?

George: "The answer is 273."

Elsie: "The answer is 183."

6 25.3 − 16.9 = ?

George: "The answer is 7.4."

Elsie: "The answer is 8.4."

3 5291 − 2922 = ?

George: "The answer is 2369."

Elsie: "The answer is 3359."

7 36.15 − 12.78 = ?

George: "The answer is 25.43."

Elsie: "The answer is 23.37."

4 6288 − 1954 = ?

George: "The answer is 5134."

Elsie: "The answer is 4334."

8 89.69 − 52.84 = ?

George: "The answer is 36.85."

Elsie: "The answer is 32.55."

Today I scored [ ] out of 8.

Year 5 Mental Maths — Autumn Term

Week 6 — Day 5

Danai is using her subtraction machine.
What answer does she get?

| 2600 | SUBTRACT | 459 rounded to the nearest 100 | = | 2100 |

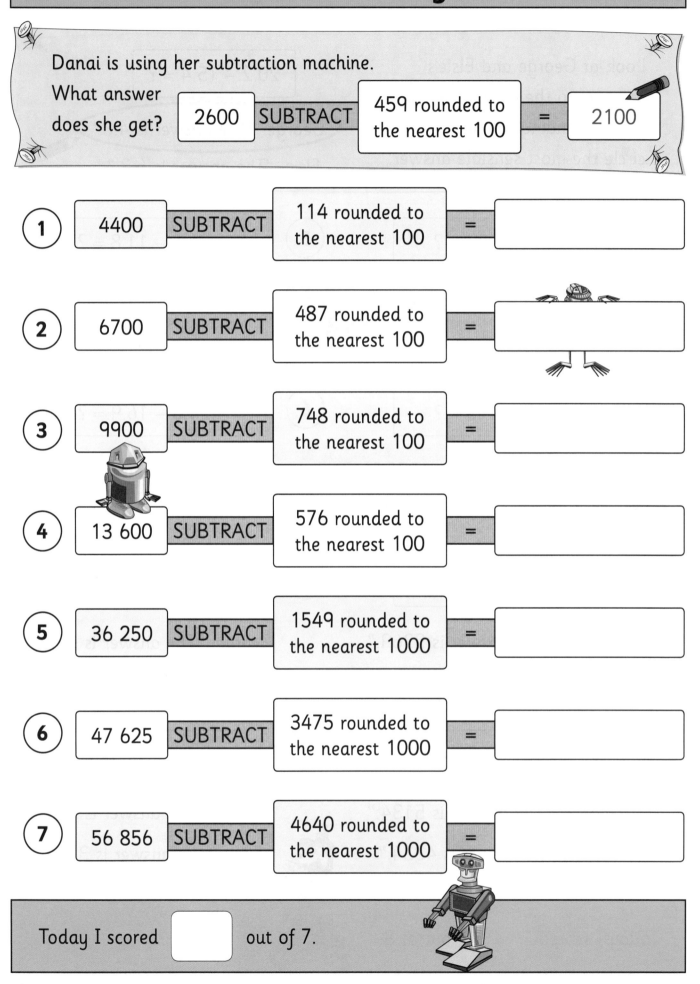

1 | 4400 | SUBTRACT | 114 rounded to the nearest 100 | = | |

2 | 6700 | SUBTRACT | 487 rounded to the nearest 100 | = | |

3 | 9900 | SUBTRACT | 748 rounded to the nearest 100 | = | |

4 | 13 600 | SUBTRACT | 576 rounded to the nearest 100 | = | |

5 | 36 250 | SUBTRACT | 1549 rounded to the nearest 1000 | = | |

6 | 47 625 | SUBTRACT | 3475 rounded to the nearest 1000 | = | |

7 | 56 856 | SUBTRACT | 4640 rounded to the nearest 1000 | = | |

Today I scored ☐ out of 7.

Week 7 — Day 1

Does the net fold up to make a cube with a star on one face and a circle on the opposite face? Put a tick if it does or a cross if it doesn't.

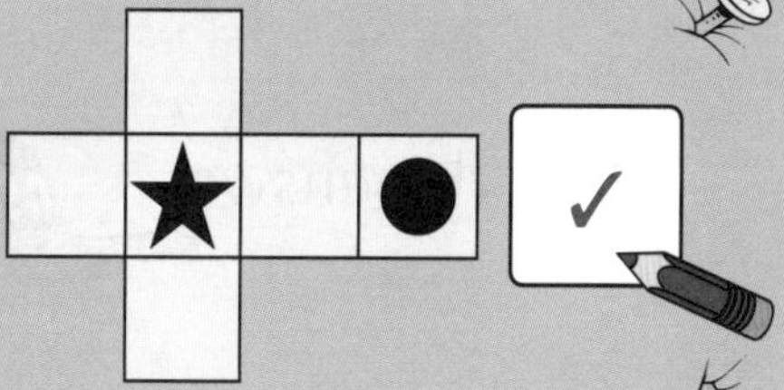

1

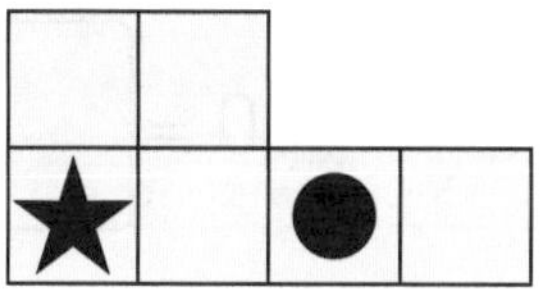

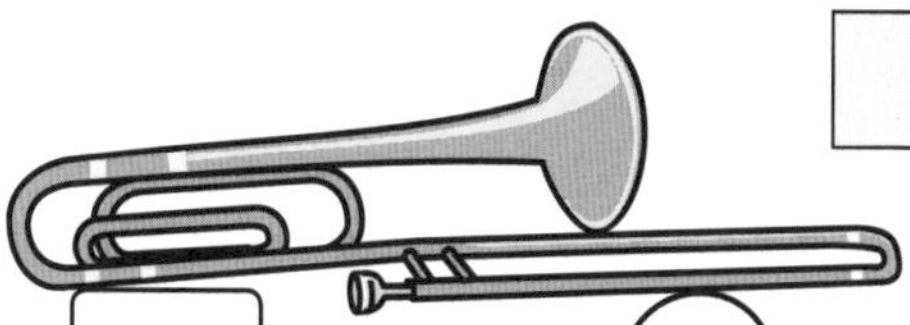

2

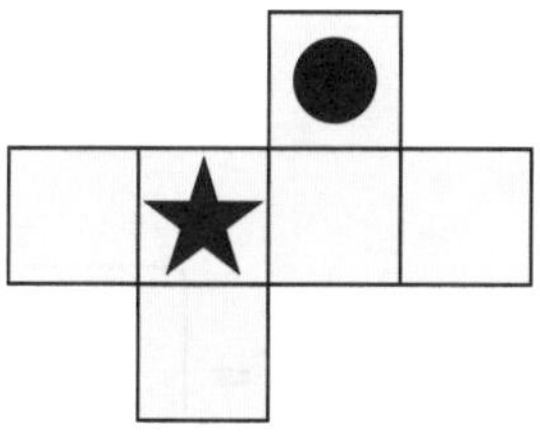

3

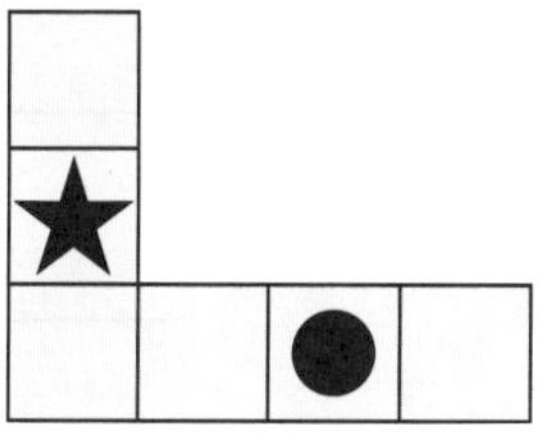

4

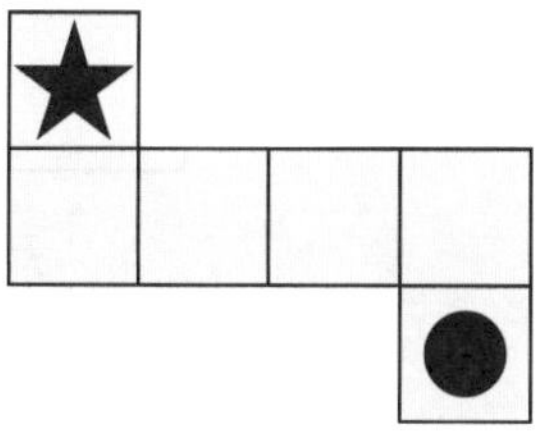

5

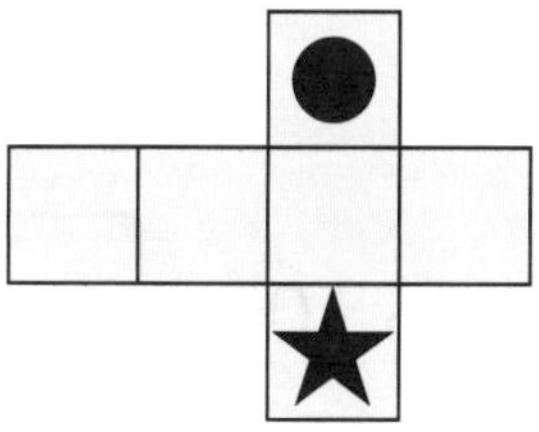

6

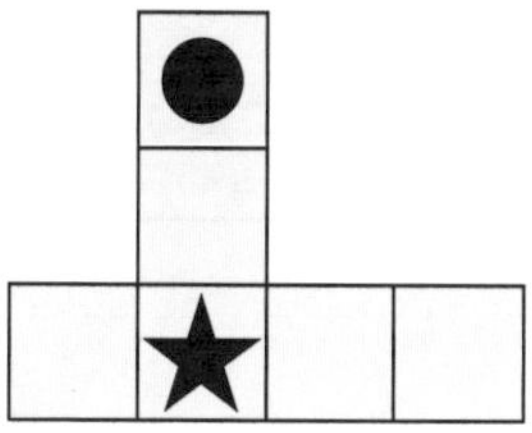

7

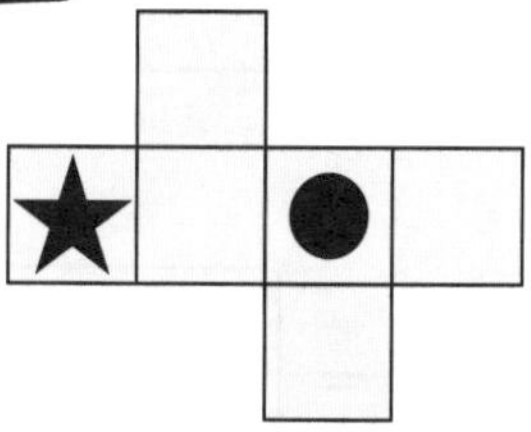

8

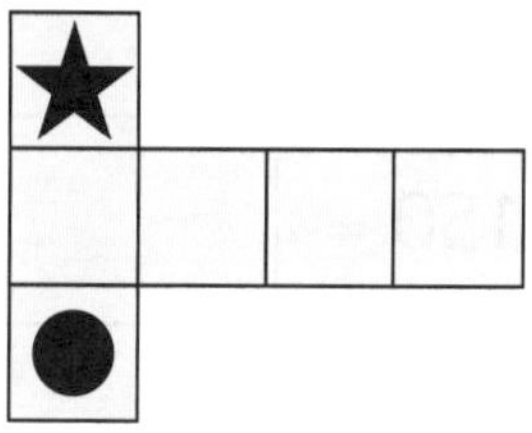

9

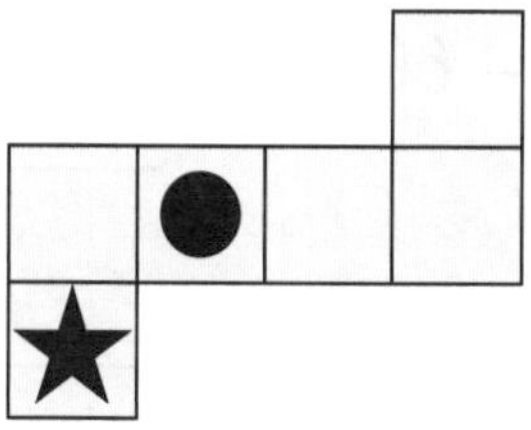

10

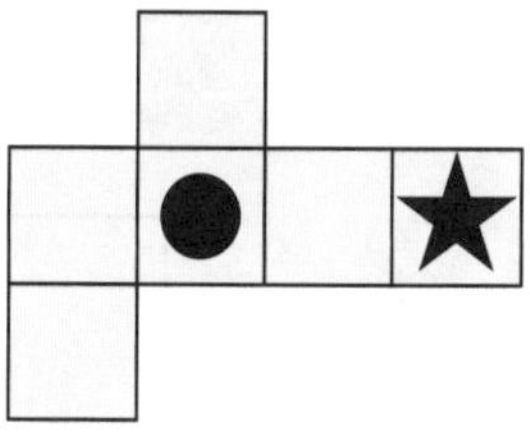

Today I scored ☐ out of 10.

Year 5 Mental Maths — Autumn Term

Week 7 — Day 2

Fill in the answer.

$1500 - 250 =$ | 1250

1. $7700 - 300 =$

2. $400 + 1200 =$

3. $800 + 2900 =$

4. $8500 - 150 =$

5. $29\ 000 - 6000 =$

6. $24\ 000 + 6000 =$

7. $37\ 000 - 8000 =$

8. $45\ 000 + 14\ 000 =$

9. $43\ 000 - 25\ 000 =$

10. $67\ 000 + 2300 =$

11. $10\ 000 - 8100 =$

12. $35\ 500 + 8500 =$

13. $84\ 000 - 5300 =$

14. $10\ 900 + 26\ 100 =$

Today I scored [ ] out of 14.

Week 7 — Day 3

Write down in centimetres how long the princess's hair will be after three days.

Princess Gold's hair is 20 cm long. It grows 10 cm each day.

After three days, it will be **50** cm.

1 Princess Blue's hair is 65 cm long. It grows 10 cm each day.

After three days, it will be [ ] cm.

2 Princess Red's hair is 210 cm long. It grows 100 cm each day.

After three days, it will be [ ] cm.

3 Princess Pink's hair is 50 cm long. It grows 25 cm each day.

After three days, it will be [ ] cm.

4 Princess Purple's hair is 230 cm long. It grows 1000 cm each day.

After three days, it will be [ ] cm.

5 Princess Orange's hair is 275 cm long. It grows 25 cm each day.

After three days, it will be [ ] cm.

6 Princess Yellow's hair is 4235 cm long. It grows 1000 cm each day.

After three days, it will be [ ] cm.

7 Princess Green's hair is 810 cm long. It grows 100 cm each day.

After three days, it will be [ ] cm.

Today I scored [ ] out of 7.

Week 7 — Day 4

Leanne is buying plants.
How much change would she get
if she paid with a £20 note?

£3.55   £3.55   £12.90

1   £9.00   £

2   £6.20   £

3   £7.25   £

4   £2.05   £7.25   £

5   £5.40   £5.40   £

6   £5.40   £9.00   £

7   £3.55   £6.20   £

8   £6.20   £6.20   £6.20   £

9   £7.25   £9.00   £

10   £2.05   £5.40   £3.55   £

Today I scored [   ] out of 10.

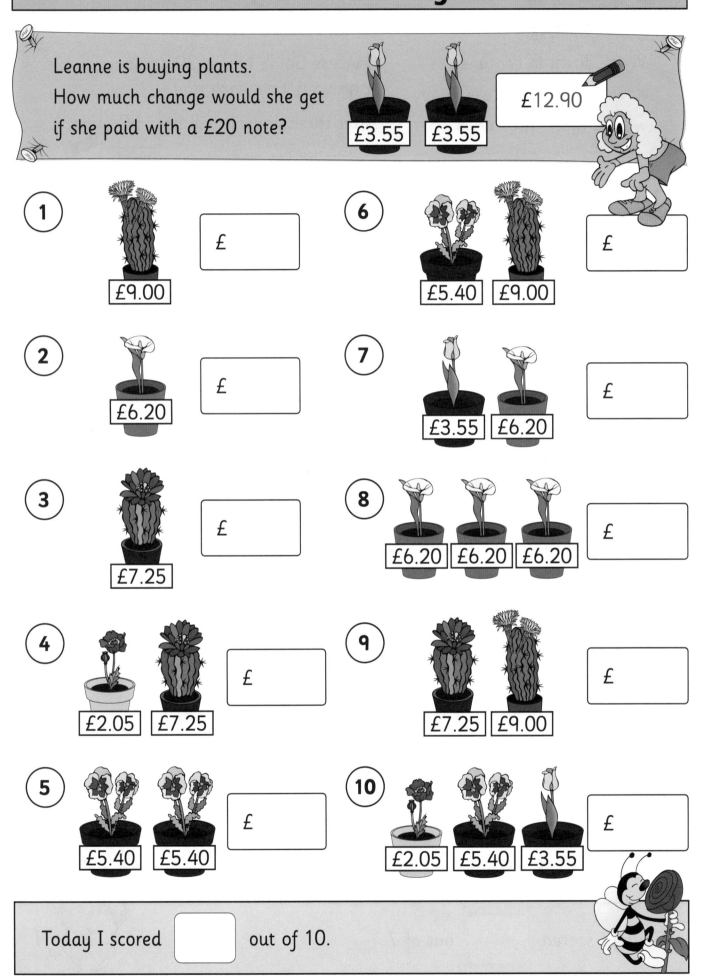

Week 7 — Day 5

Fill in the missing number.   730 + 50 = 600 +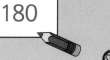

(1) 520 + 400 = 900 + ☐

(7) 25 + 850 = 700 + ☐

(2) 800 + ☐ = 320 + 600

(8) ☐ + 525 = 425 + 210

(3) ☐ + 50 = 200 + 600

(9) 910 + ☐ = 320 + 660

(4) 650 + 400 = ☐ + 800

(10) 320 + 380 = ☐ + 90

(5) 725 + ☐ = 50 + 900

(11) 125 + 225 = 240 + ☐

(6) ☐ + 750 = 650 + 350

(12) 205 + ☐ = 410 + 340

Today I scored ☐ out of 12.

Year 5 Mental Maths — Autumn Term

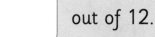

Week 8 — Day 1

Fill in the number of acute, obtuse and right angles in each shape.

acute angles [2] obtuse angles [0] right angles [1]

1 acute angles [ ] obtuse angles [ ] right angles [ ]

2 acute angles [ ] obtuse angles [ ] right angles [ ]

3 acute angles [ ] obtuse angles [ ] right angles [ ]

4 acute angles [ ] obtuse angles [ ] right angles [ ]

5 acute angles [ ] obtuse angles [ ] right angles [ ]

6 acute angles [ ] obtuse angles [ ] right angles [ ]

7 acute angles [ ] obtuse angles [ ] right angles [ ]

Today I scored [ ] out of 7.

Week 8 — Day 2

Circle the fraction which is the same as the decimal in the star.

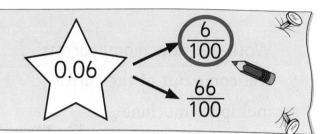

0.06 → $\frac{6}{100}$

→ $\frac{66}{100}$

1 0.63 → $\frac{63}{100}$ → $\frac{100}{63}$

2 0.53 → $\frac{100}{53}$ → $\frac{53}{100}$

3 0.18 → $\frac{18}{100}$ → $\frac{18}{10}$

4 0.27 → $\frac{27}{100}$ → $\frac{270}{100}$

5 0.88 → $\frac{8}{10}$ → $\frac{88}{100}$

6 0.04 → $\frac{40}{10}$ → $\frac{4}{100}$

7 0.33 → $\frac{33}{100}$ → $\frac{33}{10}$

8 0.9 → $\frac{99}{100}$ → $\frac{90}{100}$

9 0.02 → $\frac{2}{100}$ → $\frac{20}{100}$

10 0.5 → $\frac{5}{100}$ → $\frac{50}{100}$

11 0.3 → $\frac{3}{10}$ → $\frac{3}{100}$

12 0.8 → $\frac{8}{100}$ → $\frac{8}{10}$

Today I scored ☐ out of 12.

Year 5 Mental Maths — Autumn Term

Week 8 — Day 3

Work out how many carrots will come out of the carrot multiplier machine.

234 carrots

× 100

23 400

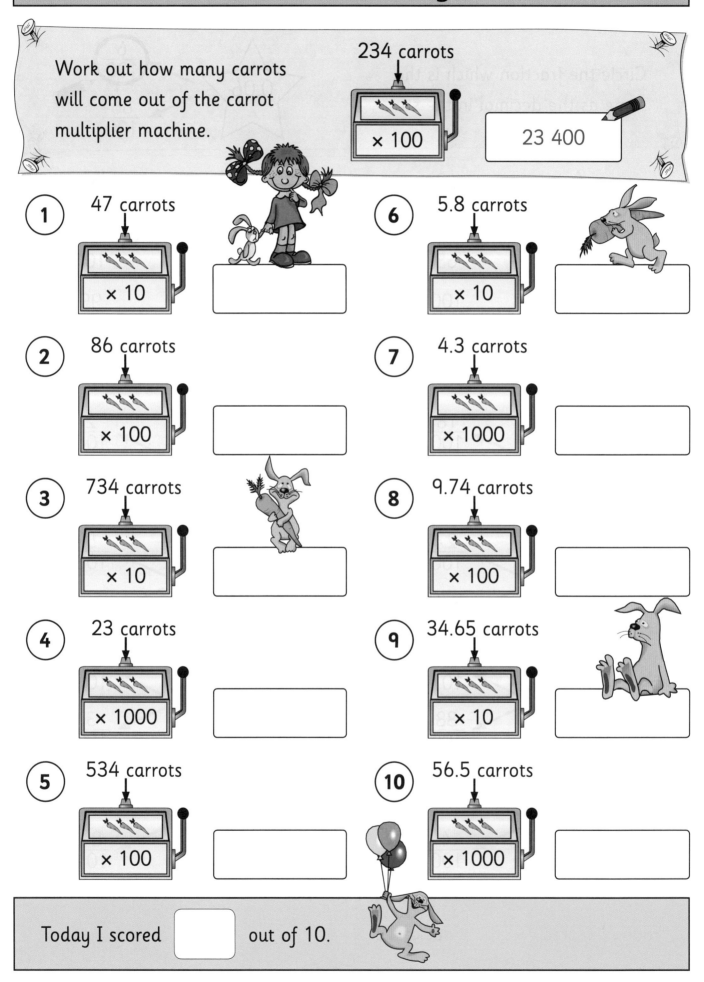

1. 47 carrots — × 10

2. 86 carrots — × 100

3. 734 carrots — × 10

4. 23 carrots — × 1000

5. 534 carrots — × 100

6. 5.8 carrots — × 10

7. 4.3 carrots — × 1000

8. 9.74 carrots — × 100

9. 34.65 carrots — × 10

10. 56.5 carrots — × 1000

Today I scored ☐ out of 10.

Week 8 — Day 4

Bertha knits items to sell. Work out how many items Bertha knits.

Bertha knits 19 gloves each week.

In 10 weeks, she knits [190] gloves.

1 Bertha knits 3 bookmarks each day.

In 1000 days, she knits [ ] bookmarks.

2 Bertha knits [ ] hats each week.

In 100 weeks, she knits 700 hats.

3 Bertha knits 2.7 jumpers each month.

In 100 months, she knits [ ] jumpers.

4 Bertha knits 0.2 cardigans each day.

In 10 days, she knits [ ] cardigans.

5 Bertha knits [ ] blankets each week.

In 100 weeks, she knits 50 blankets.

6 Bertha knits 16.5 mittens each month.

In 10 months, she knits [ ] mittens.

7 Bertha knits [ ] scarves each day.

In 1000 days, she knits 640 scarves.

Today I scored [ ] out of 7.

Week 8 — Day 5

Fill in the box to complete the sentence.

| 0.3 | is 1000 times smaller than 300.

1 800 is 100 times bigger than [ ].

2 360 is 10 times bigger than [ ].

3 [ ] is 1000 times smaller than 6000.

4 [ ] is 10 times smaller than 820.

5 562 is 10 times bigger than [ ].

6 [ ] is 100 times smaller than 3530.

7 [ ] is 1000 times smaller than 750.

8 [ ] is 1000 times smaller than 965.

9 241.4 is 10 times bigger than [ ].

10 [ ] is 10 times smaller than 523.8.

11 329.4 is 100 times bigger than [ ].

12 721.4 is 100 times bigger than [ ].

Today I scored [ ] out of 12.

Week 9 — Day 1

Fill in the answer.

What is the value of **8** in 8969?

8000

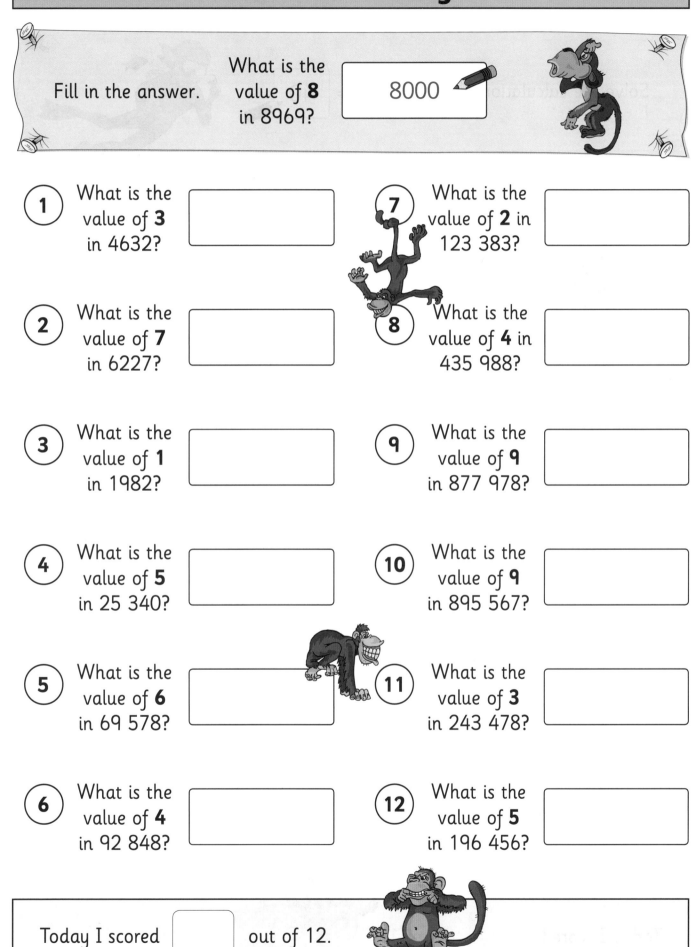

1 What is the value of **3** in 4632?

2 What is the value of **7** in 6227?

3 What is the value of **1** in 1982?

4 What is the value of **5** in 25 340?

5 What is the value of **6** in 69 578?

6 What is the value of **4** in 92 848?

7 What is the value of **2** in 123 383?

8 What is the value of **4** in 435 988?

9 What is the value of **9** in 877 978?

10 What is the value of **9** in 895 567?

11 What is the value of **3** in 243 478?

12 What is the value of **5** in 196 456?

Today I scored [ ] out of 12.

Week 9 — Day 2

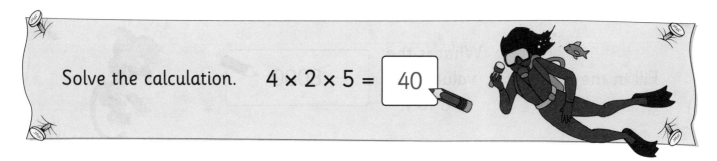

Solve the calculation. $4 \times 2 \times 5 =$ 40

1 $2 \times 3 \times 10 =$ ☐

2 $4 \times 2 \times 3 =$ ☐

3 $5 \times 2 \times 7 =$ ☐

4 $3 \times 3 \times 8 =$ ☐

5 $5 \times 9 \times 10 =$ ☐

6 $4 \times 3 \times 3 =$ ☐

7 $9 \times 7 \times 10 =$ ☐

8 $6 \times 2 \times 5 =$ ☐

9 $4 \times 3 \times 12 =$ ☐

10 $5 \times 4 \times 4 =$ ☐

11 $6 \times 5 \times 3 =$ ☐

12 $5 \times 5 \times 8 =$ ☐

Today I scored ☐ out of 12.

Week 9 — Day 3

How many lines of symmetry does the shape have?

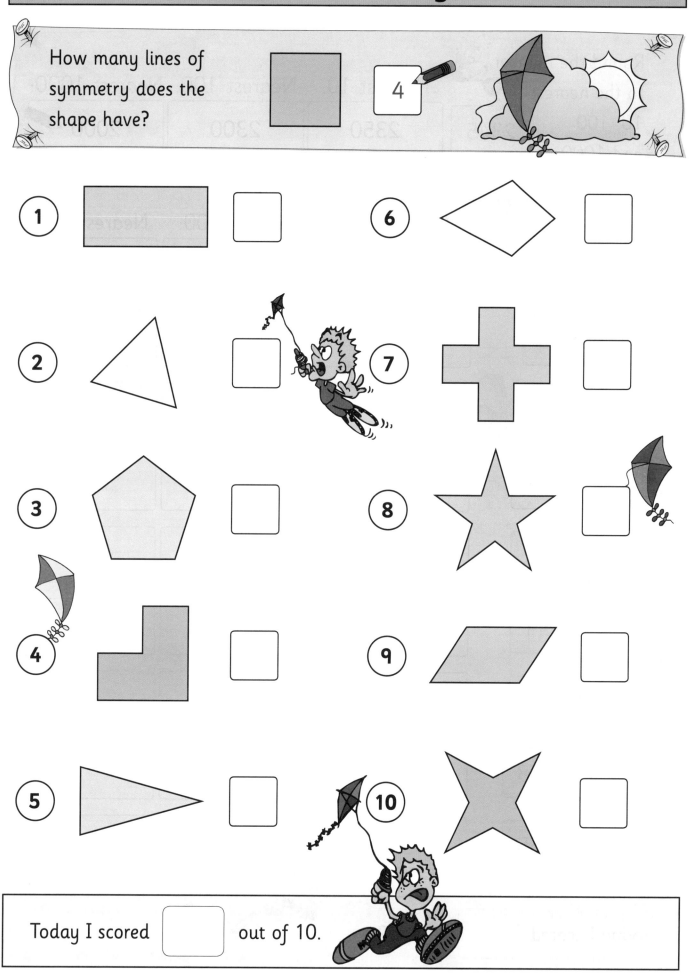

1

2

3

4

5

6

7

8

9

10

Today I scored ☐ out of 10.

Year 5 Mental Maths — Autumn Term

Week 9 — Day 4

Round the number to the nearest 10, 100 and 1000.

	Nearest 10:	Nearest 100:	Nearest 1000:
2345	2350	2300	2000

		Nearest 10:	Nearest 100:	Nearest 1000:
1	1483			
2	7455			
3	5449			
4	63 239			
5	25 654			
6	35 499			
7	99 565			
8	454 058			
9	794 555			

Today I scored [ ] out of 9.

Week 9 — Day 5

How many vegetables could the farmer have grown? Circle all the possible numbers.

A farmer grew 43 000 tomatoes to the nearest 1000.

43 543	(43 457)
(42 580)	42 451

1 A farmer grew 2300 leeks to the nearest 100.

2250	2242
2350	2349

5 A farmer grew 200 000 beans to the nearest 100 000.

155 545	145 545
245 454	254 405

2 A farmer grew 3000 potatoes to the nearest 1000.

3555	3540
2457	2500

6 A farmer grew 60 000 onions to the nearest 10 000.

55 557	64 995
54 578	65 555

3 A farmer grew 10 000 carrots to the nearest 1000.

9455	10 455
9500	10 500

7 A farmer grew 440 000 sprouts to the nearest 10 000.

445 500	435 540
444 554	434 555

4 A farmer grew 290 000 cabbages to the nearest 10 000.

295 145	284 570
285 400	294 555

8 A farmer grew 500 000 peas to the nearest 100 000.

445 550	455 540
554 450	454 450

Today I scored ☐ out of 8.

 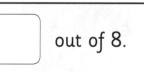

Year 5 Mental Maths — Autumn Term

Week 10 — Day 1

Fill in the answer. $\frac{1}{3}$ of 9 is [3]

(1) $\frac{1}{10}$ of 40 is [ ]

(2) $\frac{1}{5}$ of 20 is [ ]

(3) $\frac{1}{8}$ of 24 is [ ]

(4) $\frac{1}{6}$ of 42 is [ ]

(5) $\frac{3}{10}$ of 60 is [ ]

(6) $\frac{3}{4}$ of 28 is [ ]

(7) $\frac{2}{5}$ of 25 is [ ]

(8) $\frac{2}{9}$ of 36 is [ ]

(9) $\frac{3}{7}$ of 21 is [ ]

(10) $\frac{5}{12}$ of 48 is [ ]

(11) $\frac{7}{11}$ of 88 is [ ]

(12) $\frac{17}{20}$ of 40 is [ ]

(13) $\frac{6}{15}$ of 60 is [ ]

(14) $\frac{8}{25}$ of 125 is [ ]

Today I scored [ ] out of 14.

Week 10 — Day 2

Estimate the size of the angle to the nearest 10°.

60°

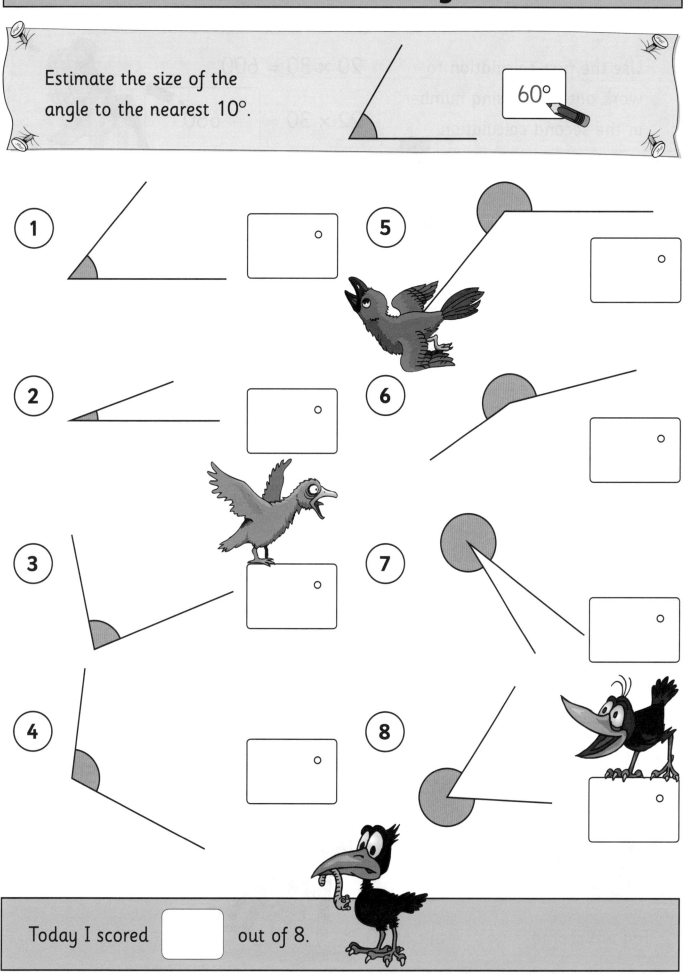

1

2

3

4

5

6

7

8

Today I scored ☐ out of 8.

Week 10 — Day 3

Use the first calculation to work out the missing number in the second calculation.

$20 \times 30 = 600$

$22 \times 30 = \boxed{660}$

1 $30 \times 30 = 900$

$31 \times 30 = \boxed{}$

6 $75 \times 40 = 3000$

$73 \times 40 = \boxed{}$

2 $40 \times 50 = 2000$

$40 \times 52 = \boxed{}$

7 $80 \times 60 = 4800$

$\boxed{} \times 60 = 4740$

3 $60 \times 20 = 1200$

$\boxed{} \times 20 = 1300$

8 $110 \times 35 = 3850$

$110 \times \boxed{} = 3960$

4 $54 \times 30 = 1620$

$\boxed{} \times 30 = 1680$

9 $140 \times 25 = 3500$

$\boxed{} \times 25 = 3425$

5 $50 \times 25 = 1250$

$50 \times \boxed{} = 1350$

10 $210 \times 105 = 22\,050$

$210 \times \boxed{} = 22\,680$

Today I scored $\boxed{}$ out of 10.

Week 10 — Day 4

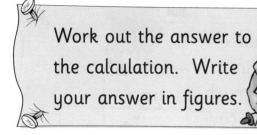

Work out the answer to the calculation. Write your answer in figures.

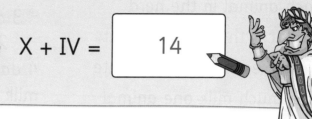

X + IV = 14

1 VIII + II =

2 X – III =

3 IV + VII =

4 XX – IX =

5 XXXV + XV =

6 L – III =

7 LX + XL =

8 C + XLIX =

9 XC – III =

10 LXVIII + IV =

11 XCIX – II =

12 XV + XXXIV =

Today I scored ⬚ out of 12.

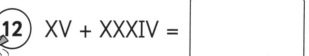

Year 5 Mental Maths — Autumn Term

Week 10 — Day 5

Each animal in the herd produces the same amount of milk each day. Calculate how much milk one animal from the herd produces.

3 cows produce 240 litres in 4 days. How much milk does each cow produce per day?

 20 l

(1) 9 reindeer produce 81 litres in 9 days.
How much milk does each reindeer produce per day?

l

(2) 4 yaks produce 64 litres in 8 days.
How much milk does each yak produce per day?

l

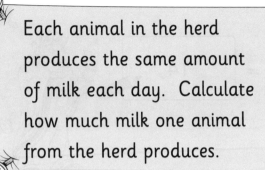

(3) 3 water buffalo produce 180 litres in 10 days.
How much milk does each water buffalo produce per day?

l

(4) 3 goats produce 63 litres in 7 days.
How much milk does each goat produce per day?

l

(5) 10 camels produce 600 litres in 4 days.
How much milk does each camel produce per day?

l

(6) 4 cows produce 176 litres in 2 days.
How much milk does each cow produce per day?

l

(7) 11 sheep produce 55 litres in 10 days.
How much milk does each sheep produce per day?

l

Today I scored [ ] out of 7.

Week 11 — Day 1

A zookeeper weighs a pair of hippos. Find the difference in weight between the two hippos.

| 3150 kg | 2130 kg |

Difference = 1020 kg

1 | 2900 kg | 2300 kg |

Difference = [ ] kg

2 | 3650 kg | 2000 kg |

Difference = [ ] kg

3 | 3800 kg | 2100 kg |

Difference = [ ] kg

4 | 3300 kg | 3150 kg |

Difference = [ ] kg

5 | 2950 kg | 1550 kg |

Difference = [ ] kg

6 | 1550 kg | 2050 kg |

Difference = [ ] kg

7 | 3200 kg | 2600 kg |

Difference = [ ] kg

8 | 3255 kg | 2140 kg |

Difference = [ ] kg

9 | 2500 kg | 4350 kg |

Difference = [ ] kg

10 | 2540 kg | 3270 kg |

Difference = [ ] kg

Today I scored [ ] out of 10.

Year 5 Mental Maths — Autumn Term

Week 11 — Day 2

Circle the two fractions inside the box that are equivalent to the fraction outside the box.

$\frac{1}{2}$ $\boxed{\frac{8}{12} \quad \cancel{\frac{2}{4}} \quad \cancel{\frac{5}{10}} \quad \frac{3}{8}}$

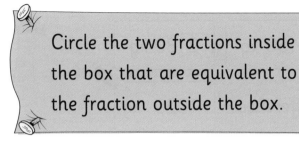

1 $\frac{1}{3}$ $\boxed{\dfrac{4}{12} \quad \dfrac{4}{9} \quad \dfrac{3}{15} \quad \dfrac{2}{6}}$

2 $\frac{1}{4}$ $\boxed{\dfrac{4}{12} \quad \dfrac{2}{8} \quad \dfrac{4}{16} \quad \dfrac{3}{9}}$

3 $\frac{2}{3}$ $\boxed{\dfrac{6}{9} \quad \dfrac{5}{15} \quad \dfrac{9}{12} \quad \dfrac{4}{6}}$

4 $\frac{2}{4}$ $\boxed{\dfrac{4}{8} \quad \dfrac{8}{14} \quad \dfrac{6}{12} \quad \dfrac{4}{6}}$

5 $\frac{3}{4}$ $\boxed{\dfrac{12}{16} \quad \dfrac{12}{18} \quad \dfrac{6}{8} \quad \dfrac{6}{5}}$

6 $\frac{2}{10}$ $\boxed{\dfrac{1}{5} \quad \dfrac{5}{20} \quad \dfrac{3}{15} \quad \dfrac{8}{30}}$

7 $\frac{2}{5}$ $\boxed{\dfrac{4}{10} \quad \dfrac{8}{15} \quad \dfrac{6}{20} \quad \dfrac{12}{30}}$

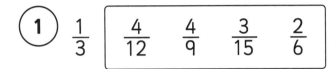

8 $\frac{1}{6}$ $\boxed{\dfrac{3}{18} \quad \dfrac{2}{3} \quad \dfrac{5}{30} \quad \dfrac{3}{12}}$

9 $\frac{1}{7}$ $\boxed{\dfrac{2}{9} \quad \dfrac{5}{35} \quad \dfrac{3}{21} \quad \dfrac{7}{14}}$

10 $\frac{4}{12}$ $\boxed{\dfrac{1}{4} \quad \dfrac{3}{6} \quad \dfrac{20}{60} \quad \dfrac{1}{3}}$

11 $\frac{2}{8}$ $\boxed{\dfrac{2}{4} \quad \dfrac{12}{48} \quad \dfrac{8}{32} \quad \dfrac{1}{16}}$

12 $\frac{1}{9}$ $\boxed{\dfrac{2}{16} \quad \dfrac{3}{27} \quad \dfrac{7}{54} \quad \dfrac{4}{36}}$

Today I scored ☐ out of 12.

Week 11 — Day 3

How much does one fruit cost?

3 pineapples cost £2.40 80 p

1 | 4 apples cost £1.60 | p

2 | 3 bananas cost £0.99 | p

3 | 6 peaches cost £5.40 | p

4 | 7 oranges cost £3.50 | p

5 | 8 mangoes cost £4.80 | p

6 | 10 melons cost £10.80 | p

7 | 6 kiwis cost £3.60 | p

8 | 8 coconuts cost £9.60 | p

9 | 9 grapefruit cost £6.30 | p

 10 | 12 papayas cost £13.20 | p

11 | 7 avocados cost £8.40 | p

12 | 30 bananas cost £9.00 | p

Today I scored [ ] out of 12.

Year 5 Mental Maths — Autumn Term

Week 11 — Day 4

Complete the calculation. $33 \times 4 =$ ┌─────┐ 132

(1) $50 \times 8 =$

(2) $13 \times 6 =$

(3) $17 \times 3 =$

(4) $14 \times 6 =$

(5) $25 \times 8 =$

(6) $88 \times 5 =$

(7) $18 \times 9 =$

(8) $19 \times 7 =$

(9) $42 \times 20 =$

(10) $15 \times 8 =$

(11) $16 \times 6 =$

(12) $18 \times 12 =$

Today I scored ☐ out of 12.

Week 11 — Day 5

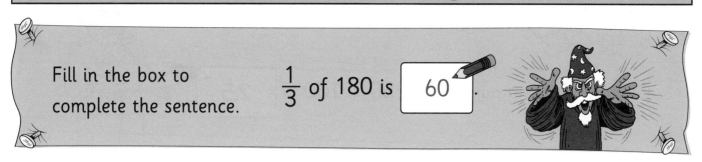

Fill in the box to complete the sentence.

$\frac{1}{3}$ of 180 is $\boxed{60}$.

1 $\frac{1}{4}$ of 120 is $\boxed{}$.

2 $\frac{1}{5}$ of 350 is $\boxed{}$.

3 $\frac{1}{\boxed{}}$ of 240 is 40.

4 $\frac{2}{3}$ of 330 is $\boxed{}$.

5 $\frac{1}{6}$ of $\boxed{}$ is 70.

6 $\frac{2}{5}$ of $\boxed{}$ is 40.

7 $\frac{4}{9}$ of 270 is $\boxed{}$.

8 $\frac{1}{8}$ of $\boxed{}$ is 80.

9 $\frac{\boxed{}}{6}$ of 300 is 200.

10 $\frac{2}{\boxed{}}$ of 810 is 180.

11 $\frac{7}{12}$ of 480 is $\boxed{}$.

12 $\frac{\boxed{}}{4}$ of 320 is 240.

Today I scored $\boxed{}$ out of 12.

Year 5 Mental Maths — Autumn Term

Week 12 — Day 1

Fill in the missing number. $250 \div 100 =$ [2.5]

---

1 $789 \div 10 =$ [ ]

2 $0.53 \times$ [ ] $= 53$

3 [ ] $\div 1000 = 64$

4 $9.87 \times 10 =$ [ ]

5 $55\ 100 \div$ [ ] $= 55.1$

6 $1.65 \times$ [ ] $= 16.5$

7 [ ] $\times 100 = 256$

8 $85\ 240 \div 1000 =$ [ ]

9 [ ] $\div 100 = 10.2$

10 $42.01 \times 100 =$ [ ]

11 $63\ 420 \div$ [ ] $= 63.42$

12 [ ] $\times 10 = 0.5$

13 $8550 \div 100 =$ [ ]

14 $52.51 \times$ [ ] $= 5251$

Today I scored [ ] out of 14.

Week 12 — Day 2

Find the perimeter
of the shape.

20 cm

10 cm

60 cm

1   30 cm

20 cm   cm

6   1.3 cm

1.2 cm   cm

2   9 cm

9 cm   cm

7   11 cm

33 cm   cm

3   10.5 cm

15 cm   cm

8   3 cm

1.1 cm   cm

4   2.5 cm

2.5 cm   cm

9   2.5 cm

4.5 cm   cm

5   9 cm

4.2 cm   cm

10   36 cm

7 cm   cm

Today I scored   out of 10.

Year 5 Mental Maths — Autumn Term

Week 12 — Day 3

Two friends are given pies of equal size. Who ate the bigger piece of pie? Annie ate $\frac{1}{4}$ of her pie. Karim ate $\frac{3}{8}$.

| Karim | ate the bigger piece.

1 Isma ate $\frac{1}{6}$ of her pie. Luke ate $\frac{1}{8}$. [   ] ate the bigger piece.

2 Zuri ate $\frac{1}{2}$ of her pie. John ate $\frac{3}{4}$. [   ] ate the bigger piece.

3 Yossi ate $\frac{2}{3}$ of his pie. Vic ate $\frac{3}{6}$. [   ] ate the bigger piece.

4 Ian ate $\frac{4}{10}$ of his pie. Amy ate $\frac{3}{5}$. [   ] ate the bigger piece.

5 Mo ate $\frac{6}{8}$ of his pie. Jan ate $\frac{4}{16}$. [   ] ate the bigger piece.

6 Lily ate $\frac{4}{5}$ of her pie. Pat ate $\frac{18}{20}$. [   ] ate the bigger piece.

7 Ivy ate $\frac{3}{7}$ of her pie. Lou ate $\frac{5}{14}$. [   ] ate the bigger piece.

8 Jo ate $\frac{5}{6}$ of her pie. Asha ate $\frac{8}{12}$. [   ] ate the bigger piece.

Today I scored [   ] out of 8.

Week 12 — Day 4

Fill in the missing number to give the fraction of the shape that has been shaded blue.

$\frac{1}{2}$

1 $\frac{2}{}$

2 $\frac{}{8}$

3 $\frac{}{2}$

4 $\frac{}{3}$

5 $\frac{1}{}$

6 $\frac{1}{}$

7 $\frac{}{4}$

8 $\frac{}{5}$

9 $\frac{6}{}$

10 $\frac{3}{}$

Today I scored [ ] out of 10.

Year 5 Mental Maths — Autumn Term

Week 12 — Day 5

Fill in the box using <, > or =.

$\dfrac{3}{24}$ $\boxed{<}$ $\dfrac{4}{16}$

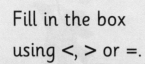

1 $\dfrac{1}{3}$ $\boxed{\phantom{<}}$ $\dfrac{3}{9}$

7 $\dfrac{5}{9}$ $\boxed{\phantom{<}}$ $\dfrac{64}{72}$

2 $\dfrac{2}{8}$ $\boxed{\phantom{<}}$ $\dfrac{8}{16}$

8 $\dfrac{5}{25}$ $\boxed{\phantom{<}}$ $\dfrac{12}{30}$

3 $\dfrac{3}{18}$ $\boxed{\phantom{<}}$ $\dfrac{2}{9}$

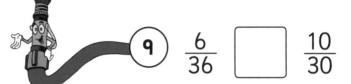

9 $\dfrac{6}{36}$ $\boxed{\phantom{<}}$ $\dfrac{10}{30}$

4 $\dfrac{2}{7}$ $\boxed{\phantom{<}}$ $\dfrac{18}{42}$

10 $\dfrac{12}{16}$ $\boxed{\phantom{<}}$ $\dfrac{24}{32}$

5 $\dfrac{3}{5}$ $\boxed{\phantom{<}}$ $\dfrac{16}{40}$

11 $\dfrac{14}{21}$ $\boxed{\phantom{<}}$ $\dfrac{40}{60}$

6 $\dfrac{4}{10}$ $\boxed{\phantom{<}}$ $\dfrac{8}{40}$

12 $\dfrac{13}{33}$ $\boxed{\phantom{<}}$ $\dfrac{30}{99}$

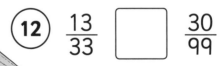

Today I scored $\boxed{\phantom{<}}$ out of 12.

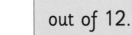

Answers

Week 1 — Day 1

1. (1, 1)
2. (3, 2)
3. (5, 4)
4. (2, 4)
5. (4, 2)
6. (0, 0)
7. (2, 0)
8. (0, 4)

Week 1 — Day 2

1. 2
2. 3
3. 1
4. 7
5. 1
6. 3
7. 6
8. 9
9. 4
10. 5
11. 0
12. 0

Week 1 — Day 3

1. 2.3 l
2. 4600 ml
3. 1500 ml
4. 520 ml
5. 6.9 l
6. 2442 ml
7. 10 l
8. 8.65 l
9. 2.51 l
10. 7.86 l
11. 5.67 l
12. 3800 ml

Week 1 — Day 4

1. $\frac{10}{9}$
2. $\frac{4}{11}$
3. $\frac{21}{10}$
4. $\frac{9}{6}$
5. $\frac{19}{5}$
6. $\frac{9}{15}$
7. $\frac{20}{40}$
8. $\frac{7}{45}$
9. $\frac{25}{60}$
10. $\frac{40}{75}$
11. $\frac{39}{28}$
12. $\frac{60}{89}$

Week 1 — Day 5

1. 10
2. 5
3. 11
4. 8
5. 20
6. 51
7. 9
8. 61
9. 75
10. 90
11. 44
12. 87

Week 2 — Day 1

1. 9, 14, 19, **24**, **29**, **34**, **39**
2. 135, 115, 95, **75**, **55**, **35**, **15**
3. 112, 2112, 4112, **6112**, **8112**, **10 112**, **12 112**
4. 228, 234, 240, **246**, **252**, **258**, **264**
5. 525, 550, 575, **600**, **625**, **650**, **675**
6. 3442, 3462, 3482, **3502**, **3522**, **3542**, **3562**
7. 860, 854, 848, **842**, **836**, **830**, **824**
8. 490, 475, 460, **445**, **430**, **415**, **400**

Week 2 — Day 2

1. £3.30
2. £8.50
3. £5.50
4. £7.00
5. £8.20
6. £7.10
7. £7.00
8. £6.20
9. £8.30
10. £10.10

Week 2 — Day 3

1. $\frac{1}{2}$
2. $\frac{1}{3}$
3. $\frac{1}{5}$
4. $\frac{1}{4}$
5. $\frac{1}{3}$
6. $\frac{1}{4}$
7. $\frac{1}{5}$
8. $\frac{1}{6}$
9. $\frac{2}{3}$
10. $\frac{2}{8}$

Week 2 — Day 4

1. 144
2. 233
3. 321
4. 605
5. 816
6. 599
7. 510
8. 120
9. 640
10. 595
11. 618
12. 335

Week 2 — Day 5

1. 40 cm
2. 4 cm
3. 3 cm
4. 10 cm
5. 30 cm
6. 8 cm

Week 3 — Day 1

1. 20 minutes
2. 35 minutes
3. 24 minutes
4. 42 minutes
5. 1 hour 2 minutes or 62 minutes
6. 2 hours 18 minutes or 138 minutes
7. 3 hours 11 minutes or 191 minutes
8. 4 hours 16 minutes or 256 minutes
9. 1 hour 45 minutes or 105 minutes
10. 3 hours 52 minutes or 232 minutes
11. 2 hours 42 minutes or 162 minutes
12. 4 hours 48 minutes or 288 minutes

Week 3 — Day 2

1. −1
2. −4
3. −1
4. −3
5. −7
6. −4
7. −6
8. −10
9. −9
10. −12
11. −14
12. −19

Week 3 — Day 3

1. 14 cm
2. 16 cm
3. 20 cm
4. 23 cm
5. 34 cm
6. 33 cm
7. 14 cm
8. 30 cm

Week 3 — Day 4

1. 2, 9
2. 4, 5
3. 3, 8
4. 1, 30
5. 4, 8
6. 5, 7
7. 4, 10
8. 4, 9
9. 2, 22
10. 7, 8
11. 8, 9
12. 8, 11

Week 3 — Day 5

1. 420
2. 7260
3. 8400
4. 9200
5. 24 300
6. 83 000
7. 11 000
8. 66 000
9. 3
10. 7
11. 13
12. 380

Week 4 — Day 1
1. 3268
2. 5356
3. 38 228
4. 47 023
5. 436 228
6. 890 012
7. 360 237
8. 472 489
9. 1 720 300
10. 1 112 783
11. 2 046 237
12. 7 234 545

Week 4 — Day 2
1. 3428
2. 42 311
3. 340 275
4. 103 069
5. 33 090
6. 714 204
7. 800 003
8. 412 060

Week 4 — Day 3
1. >
2. >
3. <
4. >
5. <
6. <
7. >
8. <
9. >
10. <
11. <
12. >
13. <
14. <

Week 4 — Day 4
1. 27 631
2. 84 792
3. 340 754
4. 303 775
5. 42 520
6. 23 040
7. 33 021
8. 789 001

Week 4 — Day 5
1. $\frac{2}{3}$
2. $\frac{3}{5}$
3. $\frac{4}{7}$
4. $\frac{3}{8}$
5. $\frac{9}{11}$
6. $\frac{5}{12}$
7. $\frac{7}{16}$
8. $\frac{3}{20}$
9. $\frac{15}{21}$
10. $\frac{12}{29}$

Week 5 — Day 1
1. 50
2. 75
3. 36
4. 36
5. 66
6. 88
7. 40
8. 72
9. 63
10. 125
11. 24
12. 39

Week 5 — Day 2
1. 4 bags
2. 2 bags
3. 9 bags
4. 11 bags
5. 9 bags
6. 25 bags
7. 20 bags
8. 15 bags
9. 11 bags
10. 6 bags

Week 5 — Day 3
1. 3 × 5
2. 3 × 8
3. 4 × 7
4. 3 × 9
5. 7 × 8
6. 5 × 9
7. 5 × 10
8. 2 × 33
9. 4 × 25
10. 3 × 24

Week 5 — Day 4
1. £15 054
2. £33 000
3. £95 325
4. £89 000
5. £19 400
6. £39 440
7. £65 020
8. £82 505
9. £88 105
10. £56 203
11. £22 100
12. £62 203

Week 5 — Day 5
1. 4
2. 5
3. 7
4. 4
5. 9
6. 9
7. 3
8. 8
9. 5
10. 7

Week 6 — Day 1
1. B
2. C
3. B
4. B
5. A
6. A

Week 6 — Day 2
1. 2 m
2. 130 cm
3. 180 g
4. 2.5 m
5. 24 m
6. 10 kg
7. 5 l
8. 300 ml
9. 150 g
10. 500 g
11. 2.3 m
12. 10 l

Week 6 — Day 3
1. 7000
2. 2000
3. 3000
4. 31 000
5. 60 000
6. 48 000
7. 7000
8. 35 000
9. 74 000
10. 56 000
11. 51 000
12. 35 000

Week 6 — Day 4
1. Elsie
2. George
3. George
4. Elsie
5. George
6. Elsie
7. Elsie
8. George

Week 6 — Day 5
1. 4300
2. 6200
3. 9200
4. 13 000
5. 34 250
6. 44 625
7. 51 856

Week 7 — Day 1

1.	✗	6.	✗
2.	✗	7.	✓
3.	✗	8.	✓
4.	✓	9.	✗
5.	✓	10.	✓

Week 7 — Day 2

1.	7400	8.	59 000
2.	1600	9.	18 000
3.	3700	10.	69 300
4.	8350	11.	1900
5.	23 000	12.	44 000
6.	30 000	13.	78 700
7.	29 000	14.	37 000

Week 7 — Day 3

1. 95 cm
2. 510 cm
3. 125 cm
4. 3230 cm
5. 350 cm
6. 7235 cm
7. 1110 cm

Week 7 — Day 4

1.	£11.00	6.	£5.60
2.	£13.80	7.	£10.25
3.	£12.75	8.	£1.40
4.	£10.70	9.	£3.75
5.	£9.20	10.	£9.00

Week 7 — Day 5

1.	20	7.	175
2.	120	8.	110
3.	750	9.	70
4.	250	10.	610
5.	225	11.	110
6.	250	12.	545

Week 8 — Day 1

1. acute angles: 2
   obtuse angles: 1
   right angles: 0
2. acute angles: 2
   obtuse angles: 2
   right angles: 0
3. acute angles: 0
   obtuse angles: 7
   right angles: 0
4. acute angles: 2
   obtuse angles: 2
   right angles: 0
5. acute angles: 0
   obtuse angles: 2
   right angles: 3
6. acute angles: 0
   obtuse angles: 3
   right angles: 2
7. acute angles: 1
   obtuse angles: 4
   right angles: 1

Week 8 — Day 2

1.	$\frac{63}{100}$	7.	$\frac{33}{100}$
2.	$\frac{53}{100}$	8.	$\frac{90}{100}$
3.	$\frac{18}{100}$	9.	$\frac{2}{100}$
4.	$\frac{27}{100}$	10.	$\frac{50}{100}$
5.	$\frac{88}{100}$	11.	$\frac{3}{10}$
6.	$\frac{4}{100}$	12.	$\frac{8}{10}$

Week 8 — Day 3

1.	470	6.	58
2.	8600	7.	4300
3.	7340	8.	974
4.	23 000	9.	346.5
5.	53 400	10.	56 500

Week 8 — Day 4

1. 3000
2. 7
3. 270
4. 2
5. 0.5
6. 165
7. 0.64

Week 8 — Day 5

1.	8	7.	0.75
2.	36	8.	0.965
3.	6	9.	24.14
4.	82	10.	52.38
5.	56.2	11.	3.294
6.	35.3	12.	7.214

Week 9 — Day 1

1.	30	7.	20 000
2.	7	8.	400 000
3.	1000	9.	900
4.	5000	10.	90 000
5.	60 000	11.	3000
6.	40	12.	50

Week 9 — Day 2

1.	60	7.	630
2.	24	8.	60
3.	70	9.	144
4.	72	10.	80
5.	450	11.	90
6.	36	12.	200

Week 9 — Day 3

1.	2	6.	1
2.	3	7.	4
3.	5	8.	5
4.	1	9.	0
5.	1	10.	4

Week 9 — Day 4

1. 1480, 1500, 1000
2. 7460, 7500, 7000
3. 5450, 5400, 5000
4. 63 240, 63 200, 63 000
5. 25 650, 25 700, 26 000
6. 35 500, 35 500, 35 000
7. 99 570, 99 600, 100 000
8. 454 060, 454 100, 454 000
9. 794 560, 794 600, 795 000

Week 9 — Day 5

1. 2250, 2349
2. 2500
3. 10 455, 9500
4. 285 400, 294 555
5. 155 545, 245 454
6. 55 557, 64 995
7. 435 540, 444 554
8. 455 540, 454 450

Week 10 — Day 1

1.	4	8.	8
2.	4	9.	9
3.	3	10.	20
4.	7	11.	56
5.	18	12.	34
6.	21	13.	24
7.	10	14.	40

Week 10 — Day 2

1. 50° (accept 40° or 60°)
2. 20° (accept 10° or 30°)
3. 80° (accept 70°)
4. 110° (accept 100° or 120°)
5. 230° (accept 220° or 240°)
6. 200° (accept 190° or 210°)
7. 340° (accept 330° or 350°)
8. 300° (accept 290° or 310°)

Week 10 — Day 3

1.	930	6.	2920
2.	2080	7.	79
3.	65	8.	36
4.	56	9.	137
5.	27	10.	108

Week 10 — Day 4

1.	10	7.	100
2.	7	8.	149
3.	11	9.	87
4.	11	10.	72
5.	50	11.	97
6.	47	12.	49

Week 10 — Day 5

1. 1 l
2. 2 l
3. 6 l
4. 3 l
5. 15 l
6. 22 l
7. 0.5 l

Week 11 — Day 1

1.	600 kg	6.	500 kg
2.	1650 kg	7.	600 kg
3.	1700 kg	8.	1115 kg
4.	150 kg	9.	1850 kg
5.	1400 kg	10.	730 kg

Week 11 — Day 2

1. $\frac{4}{12}, \frac{2}{6}$ 7. $\frac{4}{10}, \frac{12}{30}$
2. $\frac{2}{8}, \frac{4}{16}$ 8. $\frac{3}{18}, \frac{5}{30}$
3. $\frac{6}{9}, \frac{4}{6}$ 9. $\frac{5}{35}, \frac{3}{21}$
4. $\frac{4}{8}, \frac{6}{12}$ 10. $\frac{20}{60}, \frac{1}{3}$
5. $\frac{12}{16}, \frac{6}{8}$ 11. $\frac{12}{48}, \frac{8}{32}$
6. $\frac{1}{5}, \frac{3}{15}$ 12. $\frac{3}{27}, \frac{4}{36}$

Week 11 — Day 3

1.	40p	7.	60p
2.	33p	8.	120p
3.	90p	9.	70p
4.	50p	10.	110p
5.	60p	11.	120p
6.	108p	12.	30p

Week 11 — Day 4

1.	400	7.	162
2.	78	8.	133
3.	51	9.	840
4.	84	10.	120
5.	200	11.	96
6.	440	12.	216

Week 11 — Day 5

1.	30	7.	120
2.	70	8.	640
3.	6	9.	4
4.	220	10.	9
5.	420	11.	280
6.	100	12.	3

Week 12 — Day 1

1.	78.9	8.	85.24
2.	100	9.	1020
3.	64 000	10.	4201
4.	98.7	11.	1000
5.	1000	12.	0.05
6.	10	13.	85.5
7.	2.56	14.	100

Week 12 — Day 2

1.	100 cm	6.	5 cm
2.	36 cm	7.	88 cm
3.	51 cm	8.	8.2 cm
4.	10 cm	9.	14 cm
5.	26.4 cm	10.	86 cm

Week 12 — Day 3

1.	Isma	5.	Mo
2.	John	6.	Pat
3.	Yossi	7.	Ivy
4.	Amy	8.	Jo

Week 12 — Day 4

1. $\frac{2}{6}$ 6. $\frac{1}{2}$
2. $\frac{3}{8}$ 7. $\frac{2}{4}$
3. $\frac{1}{2}$ 8. $\frac{2}{5}$
4. $\frac{1}{3}$ 9. $\frac{6}{8}$
5. $\frac{1}{4}$ 10. $\frac{3}{8}$

Week 12 — Day 5

1.	=	7.	<
2.	<	8.	<
3.	<	9.	<
4.	<	10.	=
5.	>	11.	=
6.	>	12.	>

M5MWAU21